Short-Wave Listener's Guide

By
H. Charles Woodruff

FOURTH EDITION

THIRD PRINTING — 1971

International Standard Book Number: 0-672-20798-2
Library of Congress Catalog Card Number: 77-128120

PREFACE

Every owner of a short-wave receiving set is familiar with the thrill that comes from hearing a distant station broadcasting from a foreign country. To hundreds of thousands of people the world over, short-wave listening (often referred to as swl) represents the most satisfying, the most worthwhile of all hobbies.

A recently conducted survey disclosed that more than 25 million short-wave receivers are in the hands of the American public, with the number increasing daily. To explore the international short-wave broadcasting bands in a knowledgeable manner, the short-wave listener must have available a list of short-wave stations, their frequencies, and their times of transmissions. To keep abreast of the ever increasing public interest in music, news, and the exchange of cultural ideas from foreign lands, the fourth edition of *Short-Wave Listener's Guide* has again been completely revised to include the most recent changes in broadcasting schedules. The listings are conveniently arranged in four sections to help the swl'er more fully enjoy his hobby.

Section 1 consists of world-wide short-wave broadcasting stations listed alphabetically according to country and location within the country. The important particulars such as call letters (when assigned), rf carrier output in kilowatts (kW), frequency in megahertz (MHz), and hours of transmission (in Eastern Standard Time) for each station are given.

Section 2 contains a listing of short-wave broadcasting stations in numerical order by frequency, including the location and country.

Section 3 is divided into six parts, each titled with its respective time period, such as Midnight – 4:00 am EST; 4:00 am – 8:00 am EST; 8:00 am – Noon EST; Noon – 4:00 pm EST; 4:00 pm – 8:00 pm EST; 8:00 pm – Midnight EST. Within each of the six subdivisions the short-wave broadcasting stations are listed in alphabetical order by country and location. The *actual* transmission time within the respective period is also given.

Section 4 contains a listing of clandestine radio broadcasting stations that have been heard periodically. These stations either operate behind the Iron Curtain or are communist-controlled stations operating in free countries. The transmissions have been logged as they have been heard; however, for obvious reasons, their transmissions are unscheduled and sometimes may be suddenly cut off, never to be heard again.

The tabulation in this book by no means represents all of the short-wave broadcasting stations in the world. Only those normally heard in the United States are included. The accuracy cannot be guaranteed; carrier frequencies and program scheduling may change without notice. However, every effort will be made to increase the usefulness of the *Short-Wave Listener's Guide* by periodic updating. All swl'ers are cordially invited to comment on any additions, deletions, or changes that may be noted.

H. Charles Woodruff

Contents

Introduction

To pursue the very interesting and stimulating hobby of short-wave listening in an informed manner, the hobbyist must be aware of a few salient facts. These important items are discussed in the following paragraphs. Every effort has been made to simplify the data. If detailed information on a particular subject is desired it is suggested that a textbook be consulted.

Frequency

All transmission frequencies listed in this book are expressed in megahertz (MHz). While the frequencies listed in this book are carried to three decimal places for consistency, the tuning dial of most short-wave receivers will omit the decimals. For example, the numerals 9, 10, 15, 20, etc. appearing on the tuning dial stand for 9 megahertz (9 MHz), 10 megahertz (10 MHz), 15 megahertz (15 MHz), and 20 megahertz (20 MHz). To determine the location of a station broadcasting on 9.100 megahertz on the dial, the operator need only to mentally divide the space between 9 MHz and 10 MHz, and position the receiver tuning dial marker one-tenth of that spacing beyond 9 MHz. Some receivers have precision dial calibrations which are expressed in kilohertz (kHz). Megahertz frequency callouts can easily be converted to kilohertz by multiplying by 1000. Thus 9 MHz becomes 9000 kHz; 15 MHz becomes 15,000 kHz; and 9.100 MHz becomes 9100 kHz.

Some receivers may use the terms kilocycles (kc) or megacycles (mc) instead of kilohertz and megahertz. The terms are synonymous; that is "kilocycles" is the same as "kilohertz" and "megacycle" is the same as "megahertz." Formerly, the term "cycles per second" was used to designate frequencies. The terms kilocycles and megacycles (actually kilocycles per second and megacycles per second) were used to designate 1000 and 1,000,000 cycles per second. The newer term, hertz, was adopted, partially because of the fact that the "per second" portion of the previous designation was often omitted (though without the time element the term is meaningless) and partially to honor Heinrich Hertz, considered by many as the father of radio. The term *hertz* (Hz) means cycles *per second;* thus the time is included as part of the term. Likewise, kilohertz means 1000 cycles per second (1000 Hz) and megahertz means 1,000,000 cycles per second (1,000,000 Hz or 1000 kHz).

Call Letters

Any listener of conventional radio and television is aware of the call letters assigned to transmitting stations. For example KFI Los Angeles, California; KOA Denver, Colorado; WLS Chicago, Illinois; WNBC New York, New York—to name but a few. To a lesser degree this practice has also been carried over to the licensing of short-wave stations. Some (but not all) countries have assigned call letters to their high-frequency stations; however, the call letters are rarely used for station identification. Usually the announcer of a foreign short-wave station will merely say, "This is Radio Japan," "This is RSA, Radio South Africa", or "This is the Voice of America." Call letters listed in this book are for the convenience of the user, and are given only when available.

Power

Power, as listed in Section 1 of this book refers to the radio-frequency power as radiated by the antenna of the short-wave station, and is expressed in kilowatts (kW). Most international short-wave stations use transmitting equipment with a radiation power of 50 kW or more to ride through the interference and atmospheric noise. This high power does not mean that stations of 5 kW or less cannot be heard. Quite the contrary—amateur short-wave operators have repeatedly disproved this by conversing with fellow "hams" all over the world using considerably less than 1 kW of power. The unpredictableness of short-wave listening is what makes the hobby interesting and the end result more rewarding.

Wave Propagation

Two types of radio-frequency waves are emitted from a short-wave transmitting antenna—the ground wave and the sky wave. The ground wave is of no significance for short-wave reception. The sky wave, however, on leaving the transmitting antenna travels upward at various angles above the surface of the earth. It would simply continue out into space were it not bent sufficiently to bring it back to the earth. The medium which causes such bending is the ionosphere, a region in the upper atmosphere where free ions and electrons exist in sufficient quantity to cause a change in the refractive index. Ultraviolet radiation from the sun is considered to be responsible for the ionization. For a given intensity of ionization, the amount of refraction becomes less as the frequency of the wave becomes higher. The bending is smaller, therefore, at high frequency than it is at low frequencies. If the frequency is raised to a high enough value, the bending eventually will become too slight to bring the wave back to earth. At frequencies beyond this point, long-distance short-wave communication becomes impossible.

Because an increase in ionization causes an increase in the maximum frequency which can be bent sufficiently for long-distance communication, it can be seen that slight variations in sun radiation caused by sunspots, solar flares, and other solar disturbances can affect short-wave signal reception. At times, ionospheric conditions may cause a temporary "signal blackout" from some areas of the earth. Therefore, even though a station might be listed as being "on the air" for a particular time period, ionospheric conditions may prevent the signal from being heard.

Time Zones and Local Time

The United States is divided into seven standard time zones, designated as Eastern, Central, Mountain, Pacific, Yukon, Alaska/Hawaii, and Bering. These are set forth in the Uniform Time Act of 1966. The Canadian provinces occupy the first five of these seven zones, plus the Atlantic time zone on the east. In addition Newfoundland and Labrador advance the clock one-half hour ahead of the Atlantic time. The various time zones are shown on the map in Fig. 1. Each time zone is approximately 15 degrees of longitude in width and all places within a given zone use the time reckoned from the transit of the sun across the Standard Time Meridian of that zone. The time for each

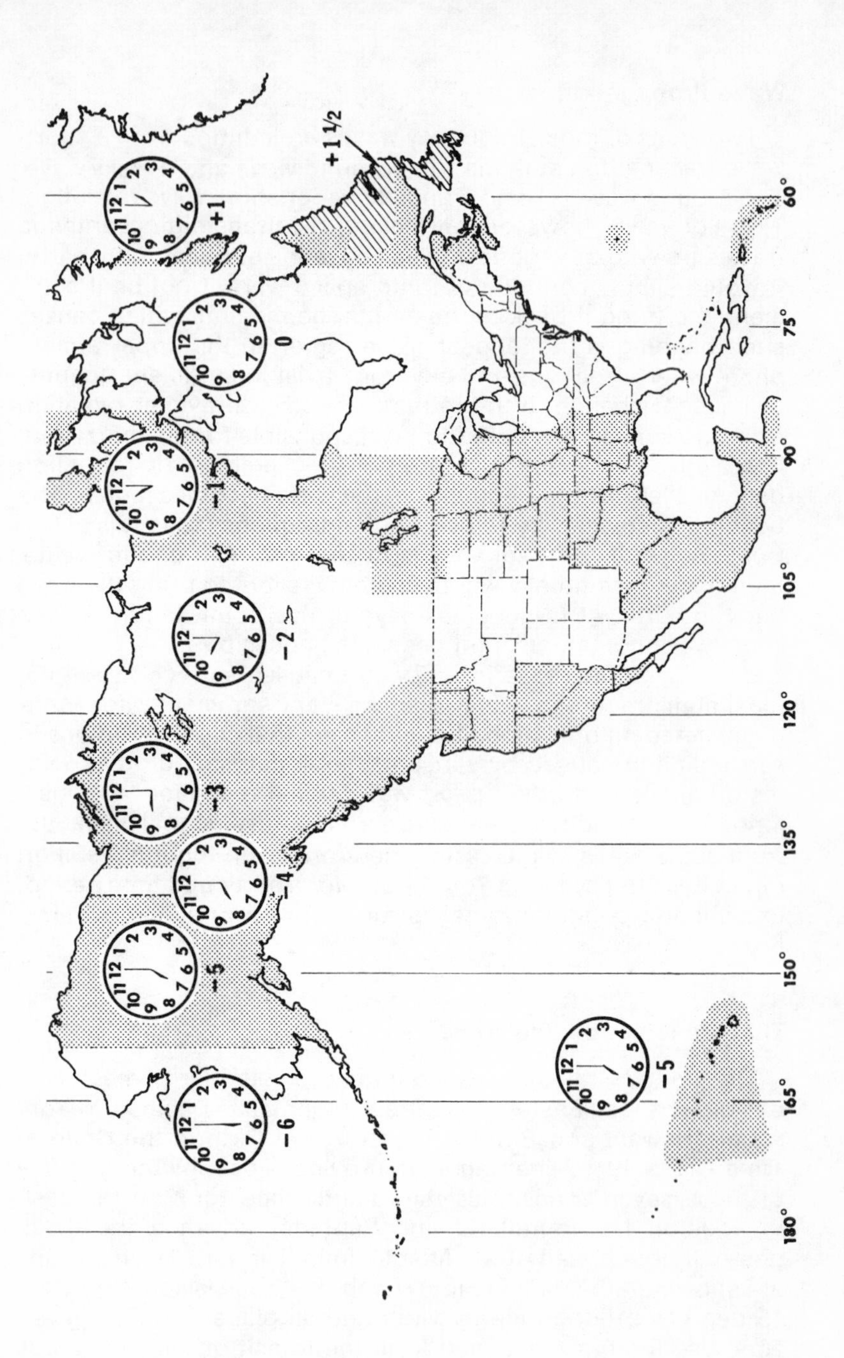

Fig. 1. Time Zones.

zone, starting with the Atlantic Time Zone and moving westward is basically reckoned from the 60th, 75th, 90th, 105th, 120th, 135th, 150th, and 165th meridian west of Greenwich, England (prime meridian). The actual division line separating the various time zones wanders somewhat from these meridians to conform with local geographic areas and local convenience.

The time of all events contained in this book is given in Eastern Standard Time (EST). To obtain the *local* time of the event when the user lives in the Atlantic Time Zone, one hour must be added to the time shown. If he lives in the Central Time Zone, one hour must be subtracted from the listed time. For local time in the Mountain Time Zone, two hours must be subtracted, etc. Fig. 1 shows the number of hours to add or subtract to obtain local time.

The time at Greenwich, England, is designated as Greenwich Mean Time (GMT) or Universal Time. This time is often used in international operations to avoid the confusion that can result in converting to local time. The time in the Eastern Time Zone is 5 hours slower than Greenwich Mean Time; that is, when it is 12 noon EST, it is 5 pm GMT.

The standard time differences for principal cities of the United States and Canada are listed in Table 1. All times listed are based on 12:00 noon EST. Table 2 gives a handy conversion from EST to the various other time zones. This table can be used in two ways. For example, if it is desired to convert a time listed in Section 1 or 3 of this book, to local time, first locate the listed time in the first (EST) column. Then read the local time directly opposite this time in the column for your time zone. Conversely, if you desire to know what stations might be broadcasting at a given local time, you can convert your local time to EST by locating the local time under the column for your local time zone and reading the EST from the left-hand column directly opposite it. For example, if it is 8 pm Pacific Daylight Time in your area and you want to know the Eastern Standard Time, first locate 8 pm in the fourth column and then opposite this point in the first column, read the Eastern Standard Time (10 pm).

The Uniform Time Act of 1966 states that Daylight Savings Time (DST) will be observed from 2:00 am on the last Sunday in April to 2:00 am on the last Sunday in October. To date, three states—Michigan, Arizona, and Hawaii—have elected to exempt themselves from the observance of Daylight Savings Time. Daylight Savings Time is achieved by *advancing* the clocks one hour. For example, an event listed here for 9:00 pm EST would take place at 10:00 pm EDT.

Table 1. Standard Time Differences

At 12 O'clock noon Eastern Standard Time, the standard time in U.S.A. and Canadian cities is as follows:

City	Time	City	Time
Akron, Ohio	12:00 Noon	Los Angeles, Calif.	9:00 am
Albuquerque, N. M.	10:00 am	Louisville, Ky.	12:00 Noon
Anchorage, Alaska	7:00 am	Memphis, Tenn.	11:00 am
Atlanta, Ga.	12:00 Noon	Miami, Fla.	12:00 Noon
Austin, Tex.	11:00 am	Milwaukee, Wis.	11:00 am
Baltimore, Md.	12:00 Noon	Minneapolis, Minn.	11:00 am
Birmingham, Ala.	11:00 am	Mobile, Ala.	11:00 am
Bismark, N. Dak.	11:00 am	Montreal, Que., Canada	12:00 Noon
Boise, Idaho	10:00 am	Nashville, Tenn.	11:00 am
Boston, Mass.	12:00 Noon	Newark, N. J.	12:00 Noon
Buffalo, N. Y.	12:00 Noon	New Haven, Conn.	12:00 Noon
Butte, Mont.	10:00 am	New Orleans, La.	11:00 am
Charleston, S. C.	12:00 Noon	New York, N. Y.	12:00 Noon
Charlotte, N. C.	12:00 Noon	Nome, Alaska	6:00 am
Chattanooga, Tenn.	12:00 Noon	Norfolk, Va.	12:00 Noon
Cheyenne, Wyo.	10:00 am	Oklahoma City, Okla.	11:00 am
Chicago, Ill.	11:00 am	Omaha, Nebr.	11:00 am
Cincinnati, Ohio	12:00 Noon	Ottawa, Onto, Canada	12:00 Noon
Cleveland, Ohio	12:00 Noon	Peoria, Ill.	11:00 am
Colorado Springs, Colo.	10:00 am	Philadelphia, Pa.	12:00 Noon
Columbus, Ohio	12:00 Noon	Phoenix, Ariz.	10:00 am
Dallas, Tex.	11:00 am	Pierre, S. Dak.	11:00 am
Dayton, Ohio	12:00 Noon	Pittsburgh, Pa.	12:00 Noon
Denver, Colo.	10:00 am	Portland, Me.	12:00 Noon
Des Moines, Ia.	11:00 am	Portland, Ore.	9:00 am
Detroit, Mich.	12:00 Noon	Providence, R. I.	12:00 Noon
Duluth, Minn.	11:00 am	Quebec, Que., Canada	12:00 Noon
Dutch Harbor, Alaska	6:00 am	Reno, Nev.	9:00 am
Edmonton, Alta., Canada	10:00 am	Richmond, Va.	12:00 Noon
El Paso, Tex.	11:00 am	Rochester, N. Y.	12:00 Noon
Erie, Pa.	12:00 Noon	Sacramento, Calif.	9:00 am
Evansville, Ind.	11:00 am	St. Louis, Mo.	11:00 am
Fairbanks, Alaska	7:00 am	St. Paul, Minn.	11:00 am
Flint, Mich.	12:00 Noon	Salt Lake City, Utah	10:00 am
Fort Wayne, Ind.	12:00 Noon	San Antonio, Tex.	11:00 am
Fort Worth, Tex.	11:00 am	San Diego, Calif.	9:00 am
Frankfort, Ky.	12:00 Noon	San Francisco, Calif.	9:00 am
Galveston, Tex.	11:00 am	Santa Fe, N. M.	10:00 am
Gander, Nfld., Canada	1:30 pm	Savannah, Ga.	12:00 Noon
Grand Rapids, Mich.	12:00 Noon	Seattle, Wash.	9:00 am
Halifax, N. S., Canada	1:00 pm	Shreveport, La.	11:00 am
Hartford, Conn.	12:00 Noon	Sioux Falls, S. Dak.	11:00 am
Helena, Mont.	10:00 am	Spokane, Wash.	9:00 am
Hilo, Hawaii	7:00 am	Tacoma, Wash.	9:00 am
Honolulu, Hawaii	7:00 am	Tampa, Fla.	12:00 Noon
Houston, Tex.	11:00 am	Toledo, Ohio	12:00 Noon
Indianapolis, Ind.	12:00 Noon	Topeka, Kan.	11:00 am
Jacksonville, Fla.	12:00 Noon	Toronto, Ont., Canada	12:00 Noon
Juneau, Alaska	9:00 am	Tucson, Ariz.	10:00 am
Kansas City, Mo.	11:00 am	Tulsa, Okla.	11:00 am
Knoxville, Tenn.	12:00 Noon	Vancouver, B. C., Canada	9:00 am
Lexington, Ky.	12:00 Noon	Washington, D. C.	12:00 Noon
Lincoln, Nebr.	11:00 am	Wichita, Kan.	11:00 am
Little Rock, Ark.	11:00 am	Wilmington, Del.	12:00 Noon
		Winnipeg, Man., Canada	11:00 am

Table 2. Time Conversion Chart

EST CDT	AST EDT	CST MDT	MST PDT	PST	YST	AST HST	BST	GMT
Midnight	1 am	11 pm	10 pm	9 pm	8 pm	7 pm	6 pm	5 am
1 am	2 am	Midnight	11 pm	10 pm	9 pm	8 pm	7 pm	6 am
2 am	3 am	1 am	Midnight	11 pm	10 pm	9 pm	8 pm	7 am
3 am	4 am	2 am	1 am	Midnight	11 pm	10 pm	9 pm	8 am
4 am	5 am	3 am	2 am	1 am	Midnight	11 pm	10 pm	9 am
5 am	6 am	4 am	3 am	2 am	1 am	Midnight	11 pm	10 am
6 am	7 am	5 am	4 am	3 am	2 am	1 am	Midnight	11 am
7 am	8 am	6 am	5 am	4 am	3 am	2 am	1 am	Noon
8 am	9 am	7 am	6 am	5 am	4 am	3 am	2 am	1 pm
9 am	10 am	8 am	7 am	6 am	5 am	4 am	3 am	2 pm
10 am	11 am	9 am	8 am	7 am	6 am	5 am	4 am	3 pm
11 am	Noon	10 am	9 am	8 am	7 am	6 am	5 am	4 pm
Noon	1 pm	11 am	10 am	9 am	8 am	7 am	6 am	5 pm
1 pm	2 pm	Noon	11 am	10 am	9 am	8 am	7 am	6 pm
2 pm	3 pm	1 pm	Noon	11 am	10 am	9 am	8 am	7 pm
3 pm	4 pm	2 pm	1 pm	Noon	11 am	10 am	9 am	8 pm
4 pm	5 pm	3 pm	2 pm	1 pm	Noon	11 am	10 am	9 pm
5 pm	6 pm	4 pm	3 pm	2 pm	1 pm	Noon	11 am	10 pm
6 pm	7 pm	5 pm	4 pm	3 pm	2 pm	1 pm	Noon	11 pm
7 pm	8 pm	6 pm	5 pm	4 pm	3 pm	2 pm	1 pm	Midnight
8 pm	9 pm	7 pm	6 pm	5 pm	4 pm	3 pm	2 pm	1 am
9 pm	10 pm	8 pm	7 pm	6 pm	5 pm	4 pm	3 pm	2 am
10 pm	11 pm	9 pm	8 pm	7 pm	6 pm	5 pm	4 pm	3 am
11 pm	Midnight	10 pm	9 pm	8 pm	7 pm	6 pm	5 pm	4 am

SECTION 1

Stations by Country and City

LOCATION	CALL LETTERS	POWER (kW)	FREQ. (MHz)	TRANSMISSION PERIOD (EST)
AFGHANISTAN				
Kabul		50	6.000	6:00 am - 8:00 am
				9:00 pm - 11:00 pm
Kabul		50	7.200	8:00 am - 1:00 pm
Kabul		100	9.510	12:30 pm - 1:30 pm
Kabul		50	11.790	12:30 pm - 1:30 pm
ALBANIA				
Tirana		50	6.200	3:30 pm - 5:00 pm
				7:00 pm - 11:00 pm
Tirana		50	7.300	7:00 pm - 11:00 pm
ALGERIA				
Algiers		50	7.125	Noon - 7:00 pm
Algiers		50	9.510	1:00 am - 7:00 pm
Algiers		30	11.730	1:00 am - 7:00 pm
Algiers		50	11.870	1:00 am - 7:00 pm
ANGOLA				
Luanda	CR6RA	100	7.265	Midnight - 9:00 pm
Luanda	CR6RB	5	9.615	5:00 am - 7:00 am
				Noon - 3:00 pm
Luanda	CR6R	100	9.660	3:00 am - 3:00 pm
Luanda	CR6RL	100	11.955	Midnight - 2:00 pm
ARGENTINA				
Buenos Aires	LRA	50	6.060	5:00 am - Midnight
Buenos Aires	LRA	100	9.690	8:00 pm - 3:00 am
Buenos Aires	LRU	100	11.710	3:00 pm - 8:00 pm
Buenos Aires	LRY	10	15.290	5:00 am - 1:00 pm

LOCATION	CALL LETTERS	POWER (kW)	FREQ (MHz)	TRANSMISSION PERIOD (EST)
ASCENSION				
Ascension		250	6.010	11:00 pm - 1:00 am
Ascension		250	9.510	5:00 pm - 11:00 pm
Ascension		250	11.820	11:00 am - 11:00 pm
Ascension		250	15.180	5:00 pm - 8:00 pm
AUSTRALIA				
Darwin	8DN	250	7.190	5:00 pm - 9:00 pm
Melbourne	VLR6	10	6.150	3:00 am - 9:00 am
Melbourne		100	9.540	10:00 am - 5:00 pm
Melbourne		100	9.560	2:00 am - 4:00 am
Melbourne	VLH9	100	9.580	7:00 am - 9:00 am
Melbourne		10	11.710	1:00 am - 4:00 am
				7:00 am - 9:00 am
Melbourne	VLH15	100	15.320	8:00 pm - 5:00 am
Melbourne		100	17.840	8:00 pm - 10:00 pm
Melbourne		100	21.740	8:00 pm - 10:00 pm
Perth	VLW6	10	6.140	5:00 am - 11:00 am
				5:00 pm - 8:00 pm
AUSTRIA				
Vienna	OEI	100	6.155	10:00 am - 8:00 am
Vienna	OEI33	100	7.245	4:00 am - 8:00 am
				3:00 pm - 5:00 pm
Vienna	OEI	100	9.770	6:00 pm - 11:00 pm
Vienna	OEI	250	11.785	8:00 am - Noon
Vienna	OEI	100	15.210	1:00 pm - 3:00 pm
Vienna	OEI	250	17.715	11:00 pm - 2:00 am
BELGIUM				
Brussels	ORU	100	6.125	8:00 pm - 10:00 pm
Brussels	ORU	100	9.550	5:00 pm - 9:00 pm
Brussels	ORU	100	11.715	8:00 am - 4:00 pm
Brussels	ORU	20	15.335	5:00 am - 2:00 pm
BOLIVIA				
La Paz	CP9	5	6.195	6:00 am - 1:00 pm
La Paz	CP38	5	9.605	6:00 am - Midnight
La Paz	CP7	10	11.765	6:00 am - 10:00 pm
BOTSWANA				
Francistown		10	5.965	11:00 pm - 5:00 pm

LOCATION	CALL LETTERS	POWER (kW)	FREQ (MHz)	TRANSMISSION PERIOD (EST)
BOTSWANA (cont.)				
Francistown		10	7.295	Midnight - Noon
BRAZIL				
Rio de Janeiro	ZYC7	100	6.115	4:00 am - 10:00 pm
Rio de Janeiro	PRL7	50	9.720	3:00 am - 11:00 pm
Rio de Janeiro		10	11.795	3:00 am - 11:00 pm
Rio de Janeiro		10	15.295	3:00 am - 11:00 pm
Rio de Janeiro	PRL9	10	17.850	3:00 am - 11:00 pm
BULGARIA				
Sofia		100	6.070	11:00 am - 6:00 pm
Sofia		50	7.255	11:00 am - 2:00 pm
Sofia		120	9.700	7:00 pm - Midnight
Sofia		50	11.765	4:00 am - 8:00 am
				11:00 am - 4:00 pm
Sofia		50	17.825	2:00 pm - 6:00 pm
BURMA				
Rangoon	XZK	50	7.120	7:00 pm - 4:00 am
Rangoon	XZK	50	9.685	11:00 pm - 3:00 am
BURUNDI				
Bujumbura		10	6.140	11:00 pm - 5:00 pm
CAMBODIA				
Phnom-Penh		50	9.695	8:00 pm - 10:00 pm
Phnom-Penh		50	11.940	7:00 pm - 9:00 pm
Phnom-Penh		50	15.255	1:00 pm - 3:00 pm
				10:00 pm - 11:00 pm
Phnom-Penh		50	17.710	12:30 am - 3:00 am
CAMEROON				
Yaoundé		4	6.005	2:00 am - Noon
Yaoundé		4	6.115	6:00 am - 3:00 pm
Yaoundé		4	7.240	2:00 am - Noon
CANADA				
Montreal	CKN	50	5.970	8:00 pm - 2:00 am
Montreal	CHA	50	5.990	1:00 am - 3:00 am
Montreal	CKY	50	9.625	9:00 pm - 2:00 am
Montreal	CHO	50	11.720	7:00 am - 10:00 am
Montreal		50	11.945	6:00 pm - 8:00 pm
Montreal	CKC	50	15.190	6:00 pm - 8:00 pm
Montreal	CKCS	50	15.320	9:00 am - 5:00 pm

LOCATION	CALL LETTERS	POWER (kW)	FREQ (MHz)	TRANSMISSION PERIOD (EST)
CANADA (cont.)				
Montreal	CKN	50	17.820	6:00 am - 1:00 pm
Toronto	CFRX	1	6.070	24 Hours
CANARY ISLANDS				
Santa Cruz		50	11.800	3:00 pm - 11:00 pm
Santa Cruz		50	15.365	3:00 pm - 11:00 pm
CAPE VERDE ISLANDS				
Sao Vincente Is.		1	6.025	3:00 am - Noon
CENTRAL AFRICAN REPUBLIC				
Bangui		4	6.100	2:00 am - Noon
Bangui		30	9.595	2:00 am - Noon
CEYLON				
Colombo		10	6.005	10:00 pm - 6:00 am
Colombo		10	7.105	6:00 am - Noon
Colombo		10	9.670	8:00 pm - 2:00 pm
Colombo		35	15.120	8:00 pm - 2:00 pm
CHAD				
Fort-Lamy		25	7.120	2:00 am - Noon
Fort-Lamy		5	9.615	2:00 am - Noon
CHILE				
Santiago	CE607	5	6.070	5:00 am - 1:00 am
Santiago	CE965	5	9.650	6:00 am - 1:00 am
Santiago	CE1197	5	11.960	5:00 am - 1:00 am
CHINA (Communist)				
Peking		100	11.685	7:00 am - 10:00 am
Peking		100	15.060	8:00 pm - Midnight
Peking		100	15.095	7:00 am - 10:00 am
				8:00 pm - Midnight
Peking		100	17.673	8:00 pm - Midnight
Peking		100	17.715	8:00 pm - Midnight
Peking		100	21.735	8:00 pm - Midnight
CHINA (Taiwan)				
Minhsiung	BEC	50	7.150	5:00 am - 2:00 pm
				7:00 pm - 10:00 pm
Panchaio	BED	25	9.685	4:00 am - 3:00 pm
Taipei	BED66	50	9.765	9:00 am - 2:00 pm
Taipei	BED37	50	11.970	10:00 am - Noon
Taipei	BED39	50	17.720	9:00 pm - 2:00 am

LOCATION	CALL LETTERS	POWER (kW)	FREQ (MHz)	TRANSMISSION PERIOD (EST)
CHINA (cont.)				
Taipei	BED40	50	17.890	9:00 pm - 11:00 pm
Tamsui	BED	7.5	6.040	5:00 am - 2:00 pm
COLOMBIA				
Bogotá	HJCF	10	5.960	6:00 am - 11:00 pm
Bogotá	HJK	10	6.125	6:00 am - Midnight
COMORO ISLAND				
Dzaoudzi		4	7.260	4:00 am - 10:00 am
CONGO, DEMOCRATIC REPUBLIC OF THE				
Kinshasa		10	6.085	11:00 pm - 3:00 pm
Kinshasa		50	7.185	10:00 am - 11:00 pm
Kinshasa		100	15.245	Midnight - Noon
CONGO, PEOPLES REPUBLIC OF THE				
Brazzaville		50	6.115	Midnight - 6:00 pm
Brazzaville		15	9.730	Midnight - 3:00 am
				Noon - 4:00 pm
Brazzaville		50	11.725	Midnight - 3:00 am
Brazzaville		50	15.145	2:00 pm - 3:00 pm
Brazzaville		50	17.785	8:00 am - Noon
COOK ISLANDS				
Rarotonga		2	9.695	2:00 pm - 7:00 pm
Rarotonga		2	11.760	2:00 pm - 6:00 pm
COSTA RICA				
San José	TIFC	5	6.007	6:00 pm - 11:00 pm
San José	TIRICA	3	9.615	6:00 am - Noon
San José	TIFC	5	9.645	7:00 am - 11:00 pm
CUBA				
Havana		50	9.525	8:00 pm - Midnight
Havana		50	11.760	10:00 pm - 1:00 am
Havana		50	11.930	1:00 am - 3:00 am
Havana		50	15.285	8:00 am - 1:00 am
Havana		50	17.750	4:00 pm - 6:00 pm
CYPRUS				
Nicosia		100	9.690	9:00 am - 1:00 pm
				10:00 pm - Midnight
Nicosia		100	11.955	8:00 pm - 11:00 pm
Nicosia		100	17.885	4:00 am - 1:00 pm

LOCATION	CALL LETTERS	POWER (kW)	FREQ (MHz)	TRANSMISSION PERIOD (EST)
CZECHOSLOVAKIA				
Prague	OLR	100	5.930	8:00 pm - 11:00 pm
Prague	OLR	100	7.345	8:00 pm - 11:00 pm
Prague	OLR	100	9.540	8:00 pm - 11:00 pm
Prague	OLR	100	9.630	8:00 pm - 11:00 pm
Prague	OLR	100	11.990	8:00 pm - 11:00 pm
DAHOMEY				
Cotonou		30	7.190	3:00 am - 1:00 pm
DOMINICAN REPUBLIC				
Santo Domingo	HIR	7.5	6.090	6:00 am - Midnight
Santo Domingo	HIZ	20	9.505	5:00 am - Midnight
ECUADOR				
Quito	HCRP1	100	5.960	9:00 pm - 2:00 am
Quito	HCJB	50	6.110	11:00 pm - 2:00 am
Quito	HCJB	30	9.745	6:00 am - 9:00 pm
Quito	HCJB	100	11.755	8:00 am - 11:00 am
Quito	HCJB	30	11.915	9:00 pm - 6:00 am
Quito	HCJB	50	15.115	9:00 pm - 10:00 pm
Quito	HCJB	50	17.880	8:00 am - Noon
EL SALVADOR				
San Salvador	YSS	5	6.010	1:00 pm - 3:00 pm
San Salvador	YSS	5	9.555	1:00 pm - 3:00 pm
ENGLAND				
London		100	5.975	Noon - Midnight
London		250	6.110	5:00 pm - Midnight
London		250	7.120	Noon - 6:00 pm
London		250	9.580	4:00 pm - 11:00 pm
London		250	11.780	10:00 am - Midnight
London		250	21.610	9:00 am - 1:00 pm
ETHIOPIA				
Addis Ababa	ETLF	100	6.185	11:00 pm - 3:00 pm
Addis Ababa	ETLF	100	7.290	11:00 pm - 3:00 pm
Addis Ababa	ETLF	100	9.695	Noon - 2:00 pm
FIJI				
Suva	VRH	10	5.955	1:00 pm - 5:00 pm
Suva	VRH	10	6.005	1:00 pm - Midnight

LOCATION	CALL LETTERS	POWER (kW)	FREQ. (MHz)	TRANSMISSION PERIOD (EST)
FINLAND				
Helsinki	OIX	15	6.120	11:00 pm - 5:00 pm
Helsinki	OIX	15	9.550	10:00 am - 2:00 pm
Helsinki	OIX	15	11.805	10:00 am - 2:00 pm
Helsinki	OIX	100	15.185	7:00 am - 11:00 am
				6:00 pm - 7:00 pm
FRANCE				
Paris		100	6.175	3:00 am - 5:00 pm
Paris		100	7.280	2:00 pm - 5:00 pm
Paris		100	15.120	8:00 am - 7:00 pm
Paris		100	21.645	6:00 am - 2:00 pm
FRENCH POLYNESIA				
Papeete		4	6.135	11:00 am - 2:00 pm
				10:00 pm - 2:00 am
Papeete		4	11.825	11:00 am - 2:00 pm
				10:00 pm - 2:00 am
GABON				
Libreville		30	7.270	2:00 am - Noon
GERMAN DEMOCRATIC REPUBLIC				
Berlin		100	5.955	8:00 pm - Midnight
Berlin		50	6.080	3:00 pm - 7:00 pm
				10:00 pm - 1:00 am
Berlin		100	9.730	8:00 pm - Midnight
Leipzig		50	9.730	5:00 am - 7:00 pm
GERMANY, FEDERAL REPUBLIC OF				
Cologne		100	6.075	11:00 am - 5:00 pm
				8:00 pm - 5:00 am
Cologne		100	6.100	7:00 pm - 2:00 am
Cologne		100	6.145	8:00 pm - 1:00 am
Cologne		100	9.655	7:00 pm - 1:00 am
Cologne		100	11.795	1:00 am - 8:00 am
Munich†		100	6.040	11:00 am - 6:00 pm
Munich†		100	7.235	1:00 pm - 6:00 pm
Munich†		50	9.750	4:00 pm - 10:00 pm
Munich†		50	9.760	9:00 am - 1:00 pm
Munich†		50	11.770	Noon - 8:00 pm
Munich†		50	15.340	Midnight - 1:00 pm
Rohrdorf		20	7.265	Midnight - 7:00 pm

†Radio Free Europe

LOCATION	CALL LETTERS	POWER (kW)	FREQ (MHz)	TRANSMISSION PERIOD (EST)
GERMANY, FEDERAL REPUBLIC OF (cont.)				
Stuttgart		20	6.030	9:00 pm - 7:00 pm
GHANA				
Tema		100	6.130	9:00 am - 5:00 pm
Tema		100	9.545	2:00 pm - 6:00 pm
Tema		250	9.760	3:00 pm - 4:00 pm
Tema		250	11.800	1:00 pm - 5:00 pm
GILBERT AND ELLICE ISLANDS				
Tarawa		5	6.055	11:00 pm - 6:00 am
GREECE				
Athens		35	9.660	10:00 am - 2:00 pm
Athens		35	9.710	6:00 am - 10:00 am
				2:00 pm - 5:00 pm
Athens		7.5	11.720	Noon - 7:00 pm
GREENLAND				
Godthaab		1	5.960	10:00 am - 9:00 pm
GRENADA				
St. George		100	11.970	6:00 pm - 10:00 pm
GUATEMALA				
Guatemala City	TGWB	5	6.180	7:00 am - 1:00 am
Guatemala City	TGNB	5	9.640	9:00 pm - 11:00 pm
GUIANA (French)				
Cayene		4	6.170	7:00 am - 2:00 pm
GUINEA (Republic)				
Conakry		18	7.125	1:00 am - 7:00 pm
Conakry		100	9.650	1:00 am - 7:00 pm
GUYANA				
Georgetown		2	5.980	6:00 am - 6:00 pm
HAITI				
Cap-Haitien		5	6.120	Noon - 9:00 pm
Port-au-Prince		1	6.050	6:00 am - 11:00 pm
HONDURAS				
Tegucigalpa	HRN	1	5.960	9:00 am - 9:00 pm
Tegucigalpa	HRLP	1	6.050	9:00 pm - 10:00 pm
Tegucigalpa	HRTV	1	6.165	7:00 am - Midnight

LOCATION	CALL LETTERS	POWER (kW)	FREQ (MHz)	TRANSMISSION PERIOD (EST)
HUNGARY				
Budapest		15	7.220	8:00 am - 2:00 pm
Budapest		100	11.910	7:00 pm - Midnight
Budapest		15	15.160	7:00 pm - Midnight
INDIA				
Delhi		100	7.105	8:00 pm - 11:00 pm
Delhi		100	7.215	Noon - 6:00 pm
Delhi		100	9.675	10:00 pm - 11:00 pm
Delhi			9.695	8:00 am - Noon
Delhi		100	10.335	10:30 am - Noon
Delhi		100	11.620	2:30 pm - 3:30 pm
INDONESIA				
Jakarta	YDF	100	6.045	5:00 am - 11:00 am
				6:00 pm - 9:00 pm
Jakarta		100	6.105	6:00 am - 11:00 am
Jakarta		10	7.210	3:00 am - 10:00 am
				3:00 pm - 7:00 pm
Jakarta		50	9.585	7:00 am - 1:00 pm
				8:00 pm - 10:00 pm
Jakarta		100	11.715	11:00 am - 3:00 pm
IRAN				
Tehran	EPB	100	15.135	3:00 am - 6:00 pm
Tehran	EPB	100	17.735	3:00 am - 4:00 pm
IRAQ				
Baghdad	YIH	100	6.030	5:00 am - 6:00 pm
Baghdad	YIH	250	7.180	5:00 am - 6:00 pm
ISRAEL				
Jerusalem	4XB49	20	7.190	6:00 am - 8:00 am
				10:00 am - 5:00 pm
Jerusalem		100	9.009	2:00 pm - 3:00 pm
Jerusalem	4XB	100	9.625	4:00 pm - 5:00 pm
Jerusalem	4XB57	100	9.725	10:00 am - 5:00 pm
ITALY				
Rome		100	5.990	10:00 am - 5:00 pm
Rome		100	6.010	5:30 pm - 7:00 pm
Rome		25	6.060	24 Hours
Rome		100	6.075	10:00 pm - 1:00 am
Rome		5	7.175	Midnight - 6:00 pm

LOCATION	CALL LETTERS	POWER (kW)	FREQ (MHz)	TRANSMISSION PERIOD (EST)
ITALY (cont.)				
Rome		60	7.290	9:00 am - 2:00 pm
Rome		5	9.515	24 Hours
Rome		60	9.575	5:00 pm - 9:00 pm
Rome		100	9.710	5:30 pm - 7:00 pm
Rome		100	11.810	8:00 pm - 10:00 pm
Rome		100	17.740	9:00 am - 1:00 pm
IVORY COAST				
Abidjan		100	6.015	1:00 am - 3:00 am
Abidjan		10	7.210	1:00 am - 7:00 pm
Abidjan		100	11.920	3:00 am - 7:00 pm
JAPAN				
Tokyo	JOB	100	9.505	11:00 pm - 2:00 pm
Tokyo	JOB-11	100	11.785	5:00 pm - 8:00 pm
Tokyo	JOB-15	100	15.105	10:00 pm - Midnight
Tokyo	JOB-15	100	15.235	9:00 pm - 10:00 pm
Tokyo	JOB	100	15.445	5:00 pm - 6:00 pm
Tokyo	JOA-17	100	17.825	5:00 pm - 6:00 pm
Tokyo	JOB	100	21.640	9:00 pm - 10:00 pm
JORDAN				
Amman		100	7.155	5:00 am - 9:00 am
				1:00 pm - 6:00 pm
Amman		100	9.530	4:00 am - 9:00 am
Amman		10	11.810	11:00 pm - 6:00 pm
Amman		100	15.170	6:30 pm - 8:00 pm
KENYA				
Nairobi	ZGW-89	5	7.125	Midnight - 9:00 am
Nairobi	ZGW-93	100	9.665	2:00 am - 9:00 am
Nairobi	ZGW	100	11.765	1:00 am - 8:00 am
KOREA				
Seoul	HLK-5	50	9.640	3:00 pm - 10:00 am
Seoul	HLK	50	15.155	1:00 am - 3:00 am
Seoul	HLK-8	50	15.430	8:00 am - 11:00 am
				8:00 pm - 11:00 pm
KUWAIT				
Kuwait	9KV-22	50	9.520	11:00 pm - 11:00 am
Kuwait	9KV	250	15.150	11:00 am - 2:00 pm
Kuwait	9KV	250	15.345	11:00 am - 1:00 pm

LOCATION	CALL LETTERS	POWER (kW)	FREQ (MHz)	TRANSMISSION PERIOD (EST)
KUWAIT (cont.)				
Kuwait	9KV	250	21.525	2:00 am - 6:00 am
LAOS				
Vientiane		10	6.130	2:00 pm - Midnight
Vientiane		10	7.145	2:00 pm - 5:00 pm
				7:00 pm - Midnight
LEBANON				
Beirut		100	11.790	9:30 pm - 10:00 pm
Beirut		100	11.820	9:00 pm - 11:00 pm
Beirut		100	11.970	1:30 pm - 2:00 pm
LIBERIA				
Monrovia	ELWA	250	7.285	10:00 pm - 3:00 am
Monrovia	ELWA	250	9.750	10:00 pm - 3:00 am
LIBYA				
Tripoli		100	6.185	Noon - 7:00 pm
Tripoli		100	7.165	24 Hours
Tripoli		100	9.565	6:00 am - 1:00 pm
LUXEMBOURG				
Junglinster	LXR	50	6.090	Midnight - 9:00 pm
Junglinster	LXR	6	15.350	Midnight - 7:00 pm
MALAGASY REPUBLIC				
Tananarive		4	7.105	Midnight - 10:00 am
Tananarive		4	7.155	Midnight - 10:00 am
Tananarive		30	9.690	Midnight - 10:00 am
MALAWI				
Zomba		10	5.995	11:00 pm - 5:00 pm
MALAYSIA				
Kuala Lumpur		100	6.175	1:00 am - 11:00 am
Kuala Lumpur		350	9.725	8:00 am - 1:00 pm
				5:00 pm - 8:00 pm
Kuala Lumpur		75	11.850	6:00 pm - 8:00 pm
Kuala Lumpur		75	11.955	4:00 am - 2:00 pm
MALI				
Bamako		50	7.285	3:00 am - 1:00 pm
Bamako		50	9.745	5:00 am - 6:00 pm
MARTINIQUE				
Fort-de-France		4	5.955	11:00 am - 9:00 pm

LOCATION	CALL LETTERS	POWER (kW)	FREQ (MHz)	TRANSMISSION PERIOD (EST)
MAURITANIA				
Nouakchott		4	7.245	3:00 am - 1:00 pm
Nouakchott		30	9.610	3:00 am - 1:00 pm
MAURITIUS				
Forest Side		10	9.710	9:00 pm - 8:00 am
MEXICO				
Leon		1	6.065	7:00 am - 1:00 am
Mexico City	XEOI	20	6.055	7:00 pm - 11:00 pm
Mexico City	XEWW	20	9.515	7:00 pm - 3:00 am
Mexico City	XEQX	20	9.530	7:00 pm - 11:00 pm
Mexico City	XEQX	1	9.555	7:00 pm - 1:00 am
Mexico City	XEMP	20	11.718	7:00 pm - 11:00 pm
Mexico City	XEMP	5	11.740	7:00 am - 1:00 am
Mexico City	XEHH	5	11.820	8:00 am - 1:00 am
MONACO				
Monte Carlo		100	5.960	1:00 am - 5:00 am
Monte Carlo		100	6.035	Midnight - 5:00 pm
Monte Carlo		30	7.135	Midnight - 5:00 pm
Monte Carlo		100	7.230	9:00 am - 2:00 pm
MOROCCO				
Tangier		100	6.170	1:00 pm - 9:00 pm
Tangier		50	7.160	10:00 pm - 1:00 am
Tangier		100	7.270	9:00 pm - 3:00 am
MOZAMBIQUE				
Lourenco Marques		3	7.130	11:00 pm - 3:00 pm
Lourenco Marques		7.5	9.670	2:00 am - 10:00 am
Lourenco Marques		8	11.780	11:00 pm - 2:00 pm
Lourenco Marques		100	15.295	9:00 am - 4:00 pm
NEPAL				
Katmandu		50	11.970	8:30 pm - Noon
NETHERLANDS				
Hilversum		100	6.140	4:00 am - 7:00 am
Hilversum		100	7.255	4:00 am - 7:00 am
Hilversum		260	9.545	10:00 pm - 1:00 am
Hilversum		300	9.715	4:00 pm - 8:00 pm
Hilversum		100	11.730	5:00 pm - 9:00 pm
Hilversum		100	15.425	4:00 pm - 8:00 pm
Hilversum		100	17.810	10:00 am - 3:00 pm

LOCATION	CALL LETTERS	POWER (kW)	FREQ (MHz)	TRANSMISSION PERIOD (EST)
NETHERLANDS ANTILLES				
Bonaire		300	9.590	7:00 pm - Midnight
Bonaire		260	9.695	9:00 pm - 11:00 pm
Bonaire		300	9.715	Midnight - 3:00 am
Bonaire		300	11.730	7:00 pm - 2:00 am
Bonaire		50	15.345	9:00 pm - 11:00 pm
NEW CALEDONIA				
Nouméa		4	7.170	1:00 am - 6:00 am
				2:00 pm - 9:00 pm
NEW HEBRIDES				
Vila		1	7.260	6:00 pm - 10:00 pm
NEW ZEALAND				
Wellington	ZL 18	7.5	9.520	3:00 am - 7:00 am
Wellington	ZL 2	7.5	9.540	1:00 am - 4:00 am
Wellington	ZL 6	7.5	15.110	3:00 pm - 7:00 pm
NICARAGUA				
Managua	YNMA	5	5.935	7:00 pm - 1:00 am
Managua	YNMA	5	9.640	6:00 am - 10:00 pm
Managua	YNMA	5	9.710	6:00 am - 11:00 pm
NIGER				
Naimey		4	7.155	2:00 am - Noon
Naimey		4	9.575	2:00 am - Noon
NIGERIA				
Enugu		10	6.145	2:00 am - Noon
Enugu		100	9.595	3:00 am - 6:00 pm
NORWAY				
Oslo	LLS	100	7.210	6:00 am - 8:00 am
Oslo	LLD	100	9.550	8:00 pm - 10:00 pm
Oslo	LLG	100	9.610	8:00 pm - Midnight
Oslo	LLG	100	9.645	9:00 pm - 10:00 pm
Oslo	LKQ	100	11.735	6:00 pm - 8:00 pm
Oslo	LLK	290	11.860	6:00 pm - 8:00 pm
PAKISTAN				
Karachi		50	7.235	2:00 pm - 4:00 pm
Karachi		50	9.735	2:00 pm - 4:00 pm
Karachi		100	15.270	6:00 am - 9:00 am
Karachi		50	17.855	8:00 am - 9:00 am
				Noon - 2:00 pm

LOCATION	CALL LETTERS	POWER (kW)	FREQ (MHz)	TRANSMISSION PERIOD (EST)
PANAMA				
Panama City	HOH-7	5	9.685	6:00 am - Midnight
PAPUA				
Port Moresby	VLT9	10	9.520	5:00 pm - 2:00 am
Rabaul	VH9RA	10	5.985	6:00 pm - 1:00 am
PARAGUAY				
Asunción	ZPA	3	9.735	6:00 am - 11:00 am
				5:00 pm - 10:00 pm
Asunción	ZPA7	5	15.210	7:00 am - Noon
				2:00 pm - 10:00 pm
PERU				
Lima	OAX4Z	10	6.080	6:00 am - 1:00 am
Lima	OAX4R	40	9.560	6:00 am - 1:00 am
Lima	OBX4R	10	11.910	6:00 am - 11:00 pm
Lima	OAX4T	10	15.150	6:00 am - 11:00 pm
PHILIPPINES				
Manila	DUH2	50	6.185	10:00 am - 6:00 pm
Manila	DZF5	50	9.715	9:00 am - 1:00 pm
				5:00 pm - 7:00 pm
Manila	DZF8	50	15.440	8:00 am - 1:00 pm
				6:00 pm - 9:00 pm
Manila	DZI6	10	17.810	5:00 pm - 7:00 pm
				9:00 pm - 5:00 am
POLAND				
Warsaw		40	5.960	6:00 am - 7:00 pm
				10:00 pm - Midnight
Warsaw		10	5.970	5:00 am - 10:00 pm
Warsaw		7.5	5.995	6:00 am - 10:00 pm
Warsaw		270	6.035	9:00 am - Midnight
Warsaw		10	7.270	1:00 pm - 11:00 pm
Warsaw		100	9.525	6:00 am - 7:00 pm
Warsaw		100	11.815	Midnight - 4:00 am
				10:00 am - 5:00 pm
Warsaw		100	15.120	9:00 am - Noon
				10:00 pm - Midnight
PORTUGAL				
Lisbon	CSB	100	6.025	2:00 pm - 4:00 pm
				7:00 pm - 3:00 am

LOCATION	CALL LETTERS	POWER (kW)	FREQ (MHz)	TRANSMISSION PERIOD (EST)
PORTUGAL (cont.)				
Lisbon	CSB	100	7.215	11:00 pm - 2:00 am
Lisbon	CSB	50	9.565	1:00 pm - 6:00 pm
Lisbon	CSB	100	9.680	7:00 pm - Midnight
Lisbon	CSB	100	11.935	7:00 pm - Midnight
RÉUNION				
Saint-Denis		4	7.245	11:00 pm - 9:00 am
RHODESIA				
Gwelo		100	7.175	Midnight - Noon
ROUMANIA				
Bucharest		20	7.195	Noon - 6:00 pm
Bucharest		120	9.510	1:00 pm - Midnight
Bucharest		120	9.570	7:00 pm - Midnight
Bucharest		120	11.940	9:00 pm - Midnight
RWANDA				
Kigali		250	15.410	7:00 am - 9:00 am
				6:00 pm - 9:00 pm
Kigali		250	15.435	1:00 pm - 5:00 pm
RYUKYU ISLANDS				
Okinawa Is.		35	6.010	5:00 am - Noon
Okinawa Is.		35	7.165	4:00 am - Noon
Okinawa Is.		100	7.235	6:00 am - Noon
SAUDI ARABIA				
Mecca		50	6.000	10:00 pm - 6:00 pm
Mecca		100	9.670	10:00 pm - 6:00 pm
Mecca		100	11.855	10:30 pm - 12:30 am
Mecca		100	15.150	10:00 pm - 5:00 pm
SENEGAL				
Dakar		100	7.210	1:00 am - 1:00 pm
Dakar		100	11.895	5:00 am - 7:00 pm
SINGAPORE				
Singapore		50	6.120	5:00 pm - 11:00 am
Singapore		10	7.170	5:00 pm - 11:00 am
Singapore		50	9.635	5:00 pm - 11:00 am
Singapore		50	11.940	7:00 pm - Noon
SOMALIA				
Hargeisa		50	7.120	5:00 am - 7:00 am
				9:00 am - 2:00 pm

LOCATION	CALL LETTERS	POWER (kW)	FREQ (MHz)	TRANSMISSION PERIOD (EST)
SOUTH AFRICA				
Johannesburg		20	7.185	Midnight - Noon
Johannesburg		250	9.705	7:00 pm - 11:00 pm
Johannesburg		250	9.715	6:00 pm - 11:00 pm
Johannesburg		250	11.875	7:00 pm - 11:00 pm
Johannesburg		250	15.220	6:00 pm - 11:00 pm
Johannesburg		250	17.825	4:00 am - 5:00 am
SPAIN				
Madrid		100	6.140	8:00 pm - 11:00 pm
Madrid		100	7.105	8:00 am - 5:00 pm
Madrid		100	9.570	8:00 am - 5:00 pm
Madrid		100	9.760	8:00 pm - 11:00 pm
SUDAN				
Omdurman		50	7.200	10:00 pm - 5:00 pm
Omdurman		50	11.835	10:00 pm - 5:00 pm
SWEDEN				
Stockholm		100	9.625	6:00 am - 7:00 am
Stockholm		100	9.725	3:30 am - 4:00 am
Stockholm		100	11.790	Midnight - 1:00 am
Stockholm		100	15.315	6:00 am - 7:00 am
				9:00 am - 10:30 am
Stockholm		100	21.585	9:00 am - 10:30 am
SWITZERLAND				
Berne		100	6.055	2:00 pm - 6:00 pm
Berne		150	6.120	9:00 pm - 1:00 am
Berne		250	6.165	1:00 am - 6:00 pm
Berne		250	9.535	Midnight - 3:00 pm
Berne		250	11.715	12:30 am - 2:00 am
Berne		250	15.305	10:00 am - Noon
Berne		250	17.830	10:00 am - Noon
SYRIA				
Damascus		50	9.660	2:00 pm - 5:00 pm
Damascus		20	11.860	6:00 pm - 1:00 am
Damascus		20	15.290	2:00 pm - 6:00 pm
				11:00 pm - 3:00 am
TAIWAN (See China)				
TANZANIA				
Dar es Salaam		10	7.280	2:00 am - 10:00 am

LOCATION	CALL LETTERS	POWER (kW)	FREQ (MHz)	TRANSMISSION PERIOD (EST)
TANZANIA (cont.)				
Dar es Salaam		20	9.530	4:00 am - 8:00 am
Zanzibar		10	9.550	6:00 am - 10:00 am
THAILAND				
Bangkok	HSK	5	7.135	10:00 pm - 9:00 am
Bangkok	HSK	100	11.910	5:00 am - 7:00 am
				11:00 pm - 1:00 am
TOGO				
Lome		100	6.155	12:30 am - 4:00 am
				7:00 am - 9:00 am
				11:30 am - 6:00 pm
Lome		100	7.265	12:30 am - 4:00 am
				7:00 am - 9:00 am
				11:30 am - 6:00 pm
TUNISIA				
Tunis		50	6.195	Noon - 7:00 pm
Tunis		50	11.970	11:00 pm - 7:00 pm
Tunis		50	17.735	3:00 am - 2:00 pm
TURKEY				
Ankara	TAT	100	9.515	11:00 am - 4:00 pm
Ankara	TAU	100	15.160	6:00 pm - 8:00 pm
				11:00 pm - 8:00 am
UGANDA				
Kampala		8	7.110	10:00 pm - 5:00 pm
UNITED ARAB REPUBLIC (Egypt)				
Cairo		100	7.265	1:00 pm - 8:00 pm
Cairo		100	9.550	1:00 pm - 8:00 pm
Cairo		100	9.580	11:00 pm - 2:00 am
Cairo		100	9.625	8:00 pm - Midnight
Cairo		100	9.740	1:00 pm - 7:00 pm
Cairo		100	11.890	1:00 pm - 7:00 pm
UNITED STATES OF AMERICA				
Cincinnati*	WLWO	250	11.810	8:00 pm - 11:00 pm
Delano*	KCBR	100	5.965	2:00 am - Noon
Delano*	KCBR	200	6.185	2:00 am - Noon
Delano*	KCBR	250	9.545	3:00 am - Noon
Delano*	KCBR	100	17.765	4:00 pm - Midnight
Dixon*	KNBH	200	6.125	3:00 am - Noon

*Voice of America

LOCATION	CALL LETTERS	POWER (kW)	FREQ (MHz)	TRANSMISSION PERIOD (EST)
UNITED STATES OF AMERICA (cont.)				
Dixon*	KNBH	100	9.605	4:00 am - Noon
Greenville*		250	9.640	5:00 pm - 8:00 pm
Greenville*		500	11.705	Midnight - 3:00 am
Greenville*		250	11.740	2:00 pm - 5:00 pm
Greenville*		250	11.845	10:00 pm - 3:00 am
Greenville*		50	21.650	5:00 am - 2:00 pm
New York*	WBOU	50	21.525	5:00 pm - 8:00 pm
UPPER VOLTA				
Ouagadougou		4	7.230	3:00 am - Noon
URUGUAY				
Montevideo		10	6.125	6:00 am - 11:00 pm
Montevideo		10	6.155	5:00 am - 10:00 pm
Montevideo		10	9.595	6:00 pm - Midnight
Montevideo		10	11.835	6:00 pm - Midnight
Montevideo		10	15.274	8:00 pm - Midnight
U.S.S.R.				
Kursk		120	11.775	6:00 pm - 1:00 am
Moscow		100	7.145	7:00 pm - 2:00 am
Moscow		240	9.530	5:00 pm - Midnight
Moscow		120	9.610	1:00 pm - 6:00 pm
				11:00 pm - 6:00 am
Moscow		240	9.655	7:00 pm - Midnight
Moscow		240	9.685	5:00 pm - 1:00 am
Moscow		240	11.870	9:00 pm - Midnight
Moscow		240	17.880	11:00 pm - 3:00 am
Omsk		50	6.190	9:00 am - 11:00 pm
Tallin		50	6.055	1:00 pm - 6:00 pm
Vladivostok		50	6.035	4:00 am - 7:00 pm
Vladivostok		240	11.850	11:00 pm - 3:00 am
U.S.S.R. (Belorussia)				
Minsk		100	9.660	1:00 am - 10:00 am
U.S.S.R. (Ukranian)				
Ivanofrankovsk		240	9.665	5:00 pm - 1:00 am
Ivanofrankovsk		100	9.760	5:00 pm - 1:00 am
Kiev		240	11.900	11:30 pm - 3:00 am
Simferopol		250	6.030	1:00 pm - 5:00 pm

*Voice of America

Short-Wave Listener's Guide

By

H. Charles Woodruff

HOWARD W. SAMS & CO., INC.
THE BOBBS-MERRILL CO., INC.
INDIANAPOLIS · KANSAS CITY · NEW YORK

LOCATION	CALL LETTERS	POWER (kW)	FREQ (MHz)	TRANSMISSION PERIOD (EST)
ITALY (cont.)				
Rome		60	7.290	9:00 am - 2:00 pm
Rome		5	9.515	24 Hours
Rome		60	9.575	5:00 pm - 9:00 pm
Rome		100	9.710	5:30 pm - 7:00 pm
Rome		100	11.810	8:00 pm - 10:00 pm
Rome		100	17.740	9:00 am - 1:00 pm
IVORY COAST				
Abidjan		100	6.015	1:00 am - 3:00 am
Abidjan		10	7.210	1:00 am - 7:00 pm
Abidjan		100	11.920	3:00 am - 7:00 pm
JAPAN				
Tokyo	JOB	100	9.505	11:00 pm - 2:00 pm
Tokyo	JOB-11	100	11.785	5:00 pm - 8:00 pm
Tokyo	JOB-15	100	15.105	10:00 pm - Midnight
Tokyo	JOB-15	100	15.235	9:00 pm - 10:00 pm
Tokyo	JOB	100	15.445	5:00 pm - 6:00 pm
Tokyo	JOA-17	100	17.825	5:00 pm - 6:00 pm
Tokyo	JOB	100	21.640	9:00 pm - 10:00 pm
JORDAN				
Amman		100	7.155	5:00 am - 9:00 am
				1:00 pm - 6:00 pm
Amman		100	9.530	4:00 am - 9:00 am
Amman		10	11.810	11:00 pm - 6:00 pm
Amman		100	15.170	6:30 pm - 8:00 pm
KENYA				
Nairobi	ZGW-89	5	7.125	Midnight - 9:00 am
Nairobi	ZGW-93	100	9.665	2:00 am - 9:00 am
Nairobi	ZGW	100	11.765	1:00 am - 8:00 am
KOREA				
Seoul	HLK-5	50	9.640	3:00 pm - 10:00 am
Seoul	HLK	50	15.155	1:00 am - 3:00 am
Seoul	HLK-8	50	15.430	8:00 am - 11:00 am
				8:00 pm - 11:00 pm
KUWAIT				
Kuwait	9KV-22	50	9.520	11:00 pm - 11:00 am
Kuwait	9KV	250	15.150	11:00 am - 2:00 pm
Kuwait	9KV	250	15.345	11:00 am - 1:00 pm

LOCATION	FREQ (MHz)	ACTUAL TIME
IVORY COAST		
Abidjan	7.210	8:00 am - Noon
Abidjan	11.920	8:00 am - Noon
JAPAN		
Tokyo	9.505	8:00 am - Noon
JORDAN		
Amman	7.155	8:00 am - 9:00 am
Amman	9.530	8:00 am - 9:00 am
Amman	11.810	8:00 am - Noon
KENYA		
Nairobi	7.125	8:00 am - 9:00 am
Nairobi	9.665	8:00 am - 9:00 am
KOREA		
Seoul	9.640	8:00 am - 10:00 am
Seoul	15.430	8:00 am - 11:00 am
KUWAIT		
Kuwait	9.520	8:00 am - 11:00 am
Kuwait	15.150	11:00 am - Noon
Kuwait	15.345	11:00 am - Noon
LIBYA		
Tripoli	7.165	8:00 am - Noon
Tripoli	9.565	8:00 am - Noon
LUXEMBOURG		
Junglinster	6.090	8:00 am - Noon
Junglinster	15.350	8:00 am - Noon
MALAGASY REPUBLIC		
Tananarive	7.105	8:00 am - 10:00 am
Tananarive	7.155	8:00 am - 10:00 am
Tananarive	9.690	8:00 am - 10:00 am
MALAWI		
Zomba	5.995	8:00 am - Noon
MALAYSIA		
Kuala Lumpur	6.175	8:00 am - 11:00 am
Kuala Lumpur	9.725	8:00 am - Noon
Kuala Lumpur	11.955	8:00 am - Noon
MALI		
Bamako	7.285	8:00 am - Noon
Bamako	9.745	8:00 am - Noon

LOCATION	FREQ (MHz)	ACTUAL TIME
MARTINIQUE		
Fort-de-France	5.955	11:00 am - Noon
MAURITANIA		
Nouakchott	7.245	8:00 am - Noon
Nouakchott	9.610	8:00 am - Noon
MEXICO		
Leon	6.065	8:00 am - Noon
Mexico City	11.740	8:00 am - Noon
Mexico City	11.820	8:00 am - Noon
MONACO		
Monte Carlo	6.035	8:00 am - Noon
Monte Carlo	7.135	8:00 am - Noon
Monte Carlo	7.230	9:00 am - Noon
MOZAMBIQUE		
Lourenco Marques	7.130	8:00 am - Noon
Lourenco Marques	9.670	8:00 am - 10:00 am
Lourenco Marques	11.780	8:00 am - Noon
Lourenco Marques	15.295	9:00 am - Noon
NETHERLANDS		
Hilversum	17.810	10:00 am - Noon
NICARAGUA		
Managua	9.640	8:00 am - Noon
Managua	9.710	8:00 am - Noon
NIGER		
Naimey	7.155	8:00 am - Noon
Naimey	9.575	8:00 am - Noon
NIGERIA		
Enugu	6.145	8:00 am - Noon
Enugu	9.595	8:00 am - Noon
PAKISTAN		
Karachi	15.270	8:00 am - 9:00 am
Karachi	17.855	8:00 am - 9:00 am
PANAMA		
Panama City	9.685	8:00 am - Noon
PARAGUAY		
Asunción	9.735	8:00 am - 11:00 am
Asunción	15.210	8:00 am - Noon

LOCATION	FREQ (MHz)	ACTUAL TIME
PERU		
Lima	6.080	8:00 am - Noon
Lima	9.560	8:00 am - Noon
Lima	11.910	8:00 am - Noon
Lima	15.150	8:00 am - Noon
PHILIPPINES		
Manila	6.185	10:00 am - Noon
Manila	9.715	9:00 am - Noon
Manila	15.440	8:00 am - Noon
POLAND		
Warsaw	5.960	8:00 am - Noon
Warsaw	5.970	8:00 am - Noon
Warsaw	5.995	8:00 am - Noon
Warsaw	6.035	9:00 am - Noon
Warsaw	9.525	8:00 am - Noon
Warsaw	11.815	10:00 am - Noon
Warsaw	15.120	9:00 am - Noon
RÉUNION		
Saint-Denis	7.245	8:00 am - 9:00 am
RHODESIA		
Gwelo	7.175	8:00 am - Noon
RWANDA		
Kigali	15.410	8:00 am - 9:00 am
RYUKYU ISLANDS		
Okinawa Is.	6.010	8:00 am - Noon
Okinawa Is.	7.165	8:00 am - Noon
Okinawa Is.	7.235	8:00 am - Noon
SAUDI ARABIA		
Mecca	6.000	8:00 am - Noon
Mecca	9.670	8:00 am - Noon
Mecca	15.150	8:00 am - Noon
SENEGAL		
Dakar	7.210	8:00 am - Noon
Dakar	11.895	8:00 am - Noon
SINGAPORE		
Singapore	6.120	8:00 am - 11:00 am
Singapore	7.170	8:00 am - 11:00 am
Singapore	9.635	8:00 am - 11:00 am

LOCATION	FREQ (MHz)	ACTUAL TIME
SINGAPORE (cont.)		
Singapore	11.940	8:00 am - Noon
SOMALIA		
Hargeisa	7.120	9:00 am - Noon
SOUTH AFRICA		
Johannesburg	7.185	8:00 am - Noon
SPAIN		
Madrid	7.105	8:00 am - Noon
Madrid	9.570	8:00 am - Noon
SUDAN		
Omdurman	7.200	8:00 am - Noon
Omdurman	11.835	8:00 am - Noon
SWEDEN		
Stockholm	15.315	9:00 am - 10:30 am
Stockholm	21.585	9:00 am - 10:30 am
SWITZERLAND		
Berne	6.165	8:00 am - Noon
Berne	9.535	8:00 am - Noon
Berne	15.305	10:00 am - Noon
Berne	17.830	10:00 am - Noon
TANZANIA		
Dar es Salaam	7.280	8:00 am - 10:00 am
Zanzibar	9.550	8:00 am - 10:00 am
THAILAND		
Bangkok	7.135	8:00 am - 9:00 am
TOGO		
Lome	6.155	8:00 am - 9:00 am
		11:30 am - Noon
Lome	7.265	8:00 am - 9:00 am
		11:30 am - Noon
TUNISIA		
Tunis	11.970	8:00 am - Noon
Tunis	17.735	8:00 am - Noon
TURKEY		
Ankara	9.515	11:00 am - Noon
UGANDA		
Kampala	7.110	8:00 am - Noon
UPPER VOLTA		
Ouagadougou	7.230	8:00 am - Noon

LOCATION	FREQ (MHz)	ACTUAL TIME
URUGUAY		
Montevideo	6.125	8:00 am - Noon
Montevideo	6.155	8:00 am - Noon
UNITED STATES OF AMERICA		
Delano*	5.965	8:00 am - Noon
Delano*	6.185	8:00 am - Noon
Delano*	9.545	8:00 am - Noon
Dixon*	6.125	8:00 am - Noon
Dixon*	9.605	8:00 am - Noon
Greenville*	21.650	8:00 am - Noon
U.S.S.R.		
Omsk	6.190	9:00 am - Noon
Vladivostok	6.035	8:00 am - Noon
U.S.S.R. (Belorussia)		
Minsk	9.660	8:00 am - 10:00 am
VATICAN		
Vatican City	6.190	11:00 am - Noon
VENEZUELA		
Caracas	6.000	8:00 am - Noon
Caracas	6.110	8:00 am - Noon
Caracas	9.640	8:00 am - Noon
Caracas	11.725	8:00 am - Noon
VIETNAM		
Saigon	7.155	8:00 am - 11:00 am
Saigon	9.620	8:00 am - 11:00 am
Saigon	11.950	8:00 am - 11:00 am
YUGOSLAVIA		
Belgrade	6.100	8:00 am - Noon
Belgrade	6.150	9:00 am - Noon
Belgrade	7.200	9:00 am - Noon
Belgrade	7.240	9:00 am - Noon
Belgrade	9.505	9:00 am - Noon
Belgrade	9.620	8:00 am - 11:00 am
Belgrade	15.235	10:00 am - 11:00 am
ZAMBIA		
Lusaka	6.165	8:00 am - Noon
Lusaka	7.220	8:00 am - 11:00 am
Lusaka	11.850	8:00 am - 9:00 am

*Voice of America

LOCATION	FREQ (MHz)	ACTUAL TIME

PART 4—Noon–4:00 pm EST

LOCATION	FREQ (MHz)	ACTUAL TIME
AFGHANISTAN		
Kabul	7.200	Noon - 1:00 pm
Kabul	9.510	12:30 pm - 1:30 pm
Kabul	11.790	12:30 pm - 1:30 pm
ALBANIA		
Tirana	6.200	3:30 pm - 4:00 pm
ALGERIA		
Algiers	7.125	Noon - 4:00 pm
Algiers	9.510	Noon - 4:00 pm
Algiers	11.730	Noon - 4:00 pm
Algiers	11.870	Noon - 4:00 pm
ANGOLA		
Luanda	7.265	Noon - 4:00 pm
Luanda	9.615	Noon - 3:00 pm
Luanda	9.660	Noon - 3:00 pm
Luanda	11.955	Noon - 2:00 pm
ARGENTINA		
Buenos Aires	6.060	Noon - 4:00 pm
Buenos Aires	11.710	3:00 pm - 4:00 pm
Buenos Aires	15.290	Noon - 1:00 pm
ASCENSION		
Ascension	11.820	Noon - 4:00 pm
AUSTRALIA		
Melbourne	9.540	Noon - 4:00 pm
AUSTRIA		
Vienna	6.155	Noon - 4:00 pm
Vienna	7.245	3:00 pm - 4:00 pm
Vienna	15.210	1:00 pm - 3:00 pm
BELGIUM		
Brussels	11.715	Noon - 4:00 pm
Brussels	15.335	Noon - 2:00 pm

LOCATION	FREQ (MHz)	ACTUAL TIME
BOLIVIA		
La Paz	6.195	Noon - 1:00 pm
La Paz	9.605	Noon - 4:00 pm
La Paz	11.765	Noon - 4:00 pm
BOTSWANA		
Francistown	5.965	Noon - 4:00 pm
BRAZIL		
Rio de Janeiro	6.115	Noon - 4:00 pm
Rio de Janeiro	9.720	Noon - 4:00 pm
Rio de Janeiro	11.795	Noon - 4:00 pm
Rio de Janeiro	15.295	Noon - 4:00 pm
Rio de Janeiro	17.850	Noon - 4:00 pm
BULGARIA		
Sofia	6.070	Noon - 4:00 pm
Sofia	7.255	Noon - 2:00 pm
Sofia	11.765	Noon - 4:00 pm
Sofia	17.825	2:00 pm - 4:00 pm
BURUNDI		
Bujumbura	6.140	Noon - 4:00 pm
CAMBODIA		
Phnom-Penh	15.255	1:00 pm - 3:00 pm
CAMEROON		
Yaoundé	6.115	Noon - 3:00 pm
CANADA		
Montreal	15.320	Noon - 4:00 pm
Montreal	17.820	Noon - 1:00 pm
Toronto	6.070	Noon - 4:00 pm
CANARY ISLANDS		
Santa Cruz	11.800	3:00 pm - 4:00 pm
Santa Cruz	15.365	3:00 pm - 4:00 pm
CEYLON		
Colombo	9.670	Noon - 2:00 pm
Colombo	15.120	Noon - 2:00 pm
CHILE		
Santiago	6.070	Noon - 4:00 pm
Santiago	9.650	Noon - 4:00 pm
Santiago	11.960	Noon - 4:00 pm

LOCATION	FREQ (MHz)	ACTUAL TIME
CHINA (Taiwan)		
Minhsiung	7.150	Noon - 2:00 pm
Panchiao	9.685	Noon - 3:00 pm
Taipei	9.765	Noon - 2:00 pm
Tamsui	6.040	Noon - 2:00 pm
COLOMBIA		
Bogotá	5.960	Noon - 4:00 pm
Bogotá	6.125	Noon - 4:00 pm
CONGO, DEMOCRATIC REPUBLIC OF		
Kinshasa	6.085	Noon - 3:00 pm
Kinshasa	7.185	Noon - 4:00 pm
Kinshasa	15.245	Noon - 4:00 pm
CONGO, PEOPLES REPUBLIC OF		
Brazzaville	6.115	Noon - 4:00 pm
Brazzaville	9.730	Noon - 4:00 pm
Brazzaville	15.145	2:00 pm - 3:00 pm
COOK ISLANDS		
Rarotonga	9.695	2:00 pm - 4:00 pm
Rarotonga	11.760	2:00 pm - 4:00 pm
COSTA RICA		
San José	9.645	Noon - 4:00 pm
CYPRUS		
Nicosia	9.690	Noon - 1:00 pm
Nicosia	17.885	Noon - 1:00 pm
DAHOMEY		
Cotonou	7.190	Noon - 1:00 pm
DOMINICAN REPUBLIC		
Santo Domingo	6.090	Noon - 4:00 pm
Santo Domingo	9.505	Noon - 4:00 pm
ECUADOR		
Quito	9.745	Noon - 4:00 pm
EL SALVADOR		
San Salvador	6.010	1:00 pm - 3:00 pm
San Salvador	9.555	1:00 pm - 3:00 pm
ENGLAND		
London	5.975	Noon - 4:00 pm
London	7.120	Noon - 4:00 pm
London	11.780	Noon - 4:00 pm

LOCATION	FREQ (MHz)	ACTUAL TIME
ENGLAND (cont.)		
London	21.610	Noon - 1:00 pm
ETHIOPIA		
Addis Ababa	6.185	Noon - 3:00 pm
Addis Ababa	7.290	Noon - 3:00 pm
Addis Ababa	9.695	Noon - 2:00 pm
FIJI		
Suva	5.955	1:00 pm - 4:00 pm
Suva	6.005	1:00 pm - 4:00 pm
FINLAND		
Helsinki	6.120	Noon - 4:00 pm
Helsinki	9.550	Noon - 2:00 pm
Helsinki	11.805	Noon - 2:00 pm
FRANCE		
Paris	6.175	Noon - 4:00 pm
Paris	7.280	2:00 pm - 4:00 pm
Paris	15.120	Noon - 4:00 pm
Paris	21.645	Noon - 2:00 pm
FRENCH POLYNESIA		
Papeete	6.135	Noon - 2:00 pm
Papeete	11.825	Noon - 2:00 pm
GERMAN DEMOCRATIC REPUBLIC		
Berlin	6.080	3:00 pm - 4:00 pm
Leipzig	9.730	Noon - 4:00 pm
GERMANY, FEDERAL REPUBLIC OF		
Cologne	6.075	Noon - 4:00 pm
Munich†	6.040	Noon - 4:00 pm
Munich†	7.235	1:00 pm - 4:00 pm
Munich†	9.760	Noon - 1:00 pm
Munich†	11.770	Noon - 4:00 pm
Munich†	15.340	Noon - 1:00 pm
Rohrdorf	7.265	Noon - 4:00 pm
Stuttgart	6.030	Noon - 4:00 pm
GHANA		
Tema	6.130	Noon - 4:00 pm
Tema	9.545	2:00 pm - 4:00 pm
Tema	9.760	3:00 pm - 4:00 pm
Tema	11.800	1:00 pm - 4:00 pm

†Radio Free Europe

LOCATION	FREQ (MHz)	ACTUAL TIME
GREECE		
Athens	9.660	Noon - 2:00 pm
Athens	9.710	2:00 pm - 4:00 pm
Athens	11.720	Noon - 4:00 pm
GREENLAND		
Godthaab	5.960	Noon - 4:00 pm
GUATEMALA		
Guatemala City	6.180	Noon - 4:00 pm
GUIANA (French)		
Cayenne	6.170	Noon - 2:00 pm
GUINEA (Republic)		
Conakry	7.125	Noon - 4:00 pm
Conakry	9.650	Noon - 4:00 pm
GUYANA		
Georgetown	5.980	Noon - 4:00 pm
HAITI		
Cap-Haitien	6.120	Noon - 4:00 pm
Port-au-Prince	6.050	Noon - 4:00 pm
HONDURAS		
Tegucipalpa	5.960	Noon - 4:00 pm
Tegucipalpa	6.165	Noon - 4:00 pm
HUNGARY		
Budapest	7.220	Noon - 2:00 pm
INDIA		
Delhi	7.215	Noon - 4:00 pm
Delhi	11.620	2:30 pm - 3:30 pm
INDONESIA		
Jakarta	7.210	3:00 pm - 4:00 pm
Jakarta	9.585	Noon - 1:00 pm
Jakarta	11.715	Noon - 3:00 pm
IRAN		
Teheran	15.135	Noon - 4:00 pm
Teheran	17.735	Noon - 4:00 pm
IRAQ		
Baghdad	6.030	Noon - 4:00 pm
Baghdad	7.180	Noon - 4:00 pm
ISRAEL		
Jerusalem	7.190	Noon - 4:00 pm

LOCATION	FREQ (MHz)	ACTUAL TIME
ISRAEL (cont.)		
Jerusalem	9.009	2:00 pm - 3:00 pm
Jerusalem	9.725	Noon - 4:00 pm
ITALY		
Rome	5.990	Noon - 4:00 pm
Rome	6.060	Noon - 4:00 pm
Rome	7.175	Noon - 4:00 pm
Rome	7.290	Noon - 2:00 pm
Rome	9.515	Noon - 4:00 pm
Rome	17.740	Noon - 1:00 pm
IVORY COAST		
Abidjan	7.210	Noon - 4:00 pm
Abidjan	11.920	Noon - 4:00 pm
JAPAN		
Tokyo	9.505	Noon - 2:00 pm
JORDAN		
Amman	7.155	1:00 pm - 4:00 pm
Amman	11.810	Noon - 4:00 pm
KOREA		
Seoul	9.640	3:00 pm - 4:00 pm
KUWAIT		
Kuwait	15.150	Noon - 2:00 pm
Kuwait	15.345	Noon - 1:00 pm
LAOS		
Vientiane	6.130	2:00 pm - 4:00 pm
Vientiane	7.145	2:00 pm - 4:00 pm
LEBANON		
Beirut	11.970	1:30 pm - 2:00 pm
LIBYA		
Tripoli	6.185	Noon - 4:00 pm
Tripoli	7.165	Noon - 4:00 pm
Tripoli	9.565	Noon - 1:00 pm
LUXEMBOURG		
Junglinster	6.090	Noon - 4:00 pm
Junglinster	15.350	Noon - 4:00 pm
MALAWI		
Zomba	5.995	Noon - 4:00 pm
MALAYSIA		
Kuala Lumpur	9.725	Noon - 1:00 pm

LOCATION	FREQ (MHz)	ACTUAL TIME
MALAYSIA (cont.)		
Kuala Lumpur	11.955	Noon - 2:00 pm
MALI		
Bamako	7.285	Noon - 1:00 pm
Bamako	9.745	Noon - 4:00 pm
MARTINIQUE		
Fort-de-France	5.955	Noon - 4:00 pm
MAURITANIA		
Nouakchott	7.245	Noon - 1:00 pm
Nouakchott	9.610	Noon - 1:00 pm
MEXICO		
Leon	6.065	Noon - 4:00 pm
Mexico City	11.740	Noon - 4:00 pm
Mexico City	11.820	Noon - 4:00 pm
MONACO		
Monte Carlo	6.035	Noon - 4:00 pm
Monte Carlo	7.135	Noon - 4:00 pm
Monte Carlo	7.230	Noon - 2:00 pm
MOROCCO		
Tangier	6.170	1:00 pm - 4:00 pm
MOZAMBIQUE		
Lourenco Marques	7.130	Noon - 3:00 pm
Lourenco Marques	11.780	Noon - 2:00 pm
Lourenco Marques	15.295	Noon - 4:00 pm
NETHERLANDS		
Hilversum	17.810	Noon - 3:00 pm
NEW CALEDONIA		
Nouméa	7.170	2:00 pm - 4:00 pm
NEW ZEALAND		
Wellington	15.110	3:00 pm - 4:00 pm
NICARAGUA		
Managua	9.640	Noon - 4:00 pm
Managua	9.710	Noon - 4:00 pm
NIGERIA		
Enugu	9.595	Noon - 4:00 pm
PAKISTAN		
Karachi	7.235	2:00 pm - 4:00 pm
Karachi	9.735	2:00 pm - 4:00 pm

LOCATION	FREQ (MHz)	ACTUAL TIME
PAKISTAN (cont.)		
Karachi	17.855	Noon - 2:00 pm
PANAMA		
Panama City	9.685	Noon - 4:00 pm
PARAGUAY		
Asunción	15.210	2:00 pm - 4:00 pm
PERU		
Lima	6.080	Noon - 4:00 pm
Lima	9.560	Noon - 4:00 pm
Lima	11.910	Noon - 4:00 pm
Lima	15.150	Noon - 4:00 pm
PHILIPPINES		
Manila	6.185	Noon - 4:00 pm
Manila	9.715	Noon - 1:00 pm
Manila	15.440	Noon - 1:00 pm
POLAND		
Warsaw	5.960	Noon - 4:00 pm
Warsaw	5.970	Noon - 4:00 pm
Warsaw	5.995	Noon - 4:00 pm
Warsaw	6.035	Noon - 4:00 pm
Warsaw	7.270	1:00 pm - 4:00 pm
Warsaw	9.525	Noon - 4:00 pm
Warsaw	11.815	Noon - 4:00 pm
PORTUGAL		
Lisbon	6.025	2:00 pm - 4:00 pm
Lisbon	9.565	1:00 pm - 4:00 pm
ROMANIA		
Bucharest	7.195	Noon - 4:00 pm
Bucharest	9.510	1:00 pm - 4:00 pm
RWANDA		
Kigali	15.435	1:00 pm - 4:00 pm
SAUDI ARABIA		
Mecca	6.000	Noon - 4:00 pm
Mecca	9.670	Noon - 4:00 pm
Mecca	15.150	Noon - 4:00 pm
SENEGAL		
Dakar	7.210	Noon - 1:00 pm
Dakar	11.895	Noon - 4:00 pm

LOCATION	FREQ (MHz)	ACTUAL TIME
SOMALIA		
Hargeisa	7.120	Noon - 2:00 pm
SPAIN		
Madrid	7.105	Noon - 4:00 pm
Madrid	9.570	Noon - 4:00 pm
SUDAN		
Omdurman	7.200	Noon - 4:00 pm
Omdurman	11.835	Noon - 4:00 pm
SWITZERLAND		
Berne	6.055	2:00 pm - 4:00 pm
Berne	6.165	Noon - 4:00 pm
Berne	9.535	Noon - 3:00 pm
SYRIA		
Damascus	9.660	2:00 pm - 4:00 pm
Damascus	15.290	2:00 pm - 4:00 pm
TOGO		
Lome	6.155	Noon - 4:00 pm
Lome	7.265	Noon - 4:00 pm
TUNISIA		
Tunis	6.195	Noon - 4:00 pm
Tunis	11.970	Noon - 4:00 pm
Tunis	17.735	Noon - 2:00 pm
TURKEY		
Ankara	9.515	Noon - 4:00 pm
UGANDA		
Kampala	7.110	Noon - 4:00 pm
UNITED ARAB REPUBLIC		
Cairo	7.265	1:00 pm - 4:00 pm
Cairo	9.550	1:00 pm - 4:00 pm
Cairo	9.740	1:00 pm - 4:00 pm
Cairo	11.890	1:00 pm - 4:00 pm
URUGUAY		
Montevideo	6.125	Noon - 4:00 pm
Montevideo	6.155	Noon - 4:00 pm
UNITED STATES OF AMERICA		
Greenville*	11.740	2:00 pm - 4:00 pm
Greenville*	21.650	Noon - 2:00 pm

*Voice of America

LOCATION	FREQ (MHz)	ACTUAL TIME
U.S.S.R.		
Moscow	9.610	1:00 pm - 4:00 pm
Omsk	6.190	Noon - 4:00 pm
Tallin	6.055	1:00 pm - 4:00 pm
Vladivostok	6.035	Noon - 4:00 pm
U.S.S.R. (Ukrainian)		
Simferopol	6.030	1:00 pm - 4:00 pm
VATICAN		
Vatican City	6.190	Noon - 4:00 pm
VENEZUELA		
Caracas	6.000	Noon - 4:00 pm
Caracas	6.110	Noon - 4:00 pm
Caracas	9.640	Noon - 4:00 pm
Caracas	11.725	Noon - 4:00 pm
YUGOSLAVIA		
Belgrade	6.100	Noon - 4:00 pm
Belgrade	6.110	1:00 pm - 4:00 pm
Belgrade	6.150	Noon - 4:00 pm
Belgrade	7.200	Noon - 4:00 pm
Belgrade	7.240	Noon - 4:00 pm
Belgrade	9.505	Noon - 4:00 pm
Belgrade	9.620	1:00 pm - 4:00 pm
ZAMBIA		
Lusaka	6.165	Noon - 4:00 pm

PART 5—4:00 pm–8:00 pm EST

ALBANIA		
Tirana	6.200	4:00 pm - 5:00 pm 7:00 pm - 8:00 pm
Tirana	7.300	7:00 pm - 8:00 pm
ALGERIA		
Algiers	7.125	4:00 pm - 7:00 pm
Algiers	9.510	4:00 pm - 7:00 pm
Algiers	11.730	4:00 pm - 7:00 pm

LOCATION	FREQ (MHz)	ACTUAL TIME
ALGERIA (cont.)		
Algiers	11.870	4:00 pm - 7:00 pm
ANGOLA		
Luanda	7.265	4:00 pm - 8:00 pm
ARGENTINA		
Buenos Aires	6.060	4:00 pm - 8:00 pm
Buenos Aires	11.710	4:00 pm - 8:00 pm
ASCENSION		
Ascension	9.510	5:00 pm - 8:00 pm
Ascension	11.820	4:00 pm - 8:00 pm
Ascension	15.180	5:00 pm - 8:00 pm
AUSTRALIA		
Darwin	7.190	5:00 pm - 8:00 pm
Melbourne	9.540	4:00 pm - 5:00 pm
Perth	6.140	5:00 pm - 8:00 pm
AUSTRIA		
Vienna	6.155	4:00 pm - 8:00 pm
Vienna	7.245	4:00 pm - 5:00 pm
Vienna	9.770	6:00 pm - 8:00 pm
BELGIUM		
Brussels	9.550	5:00 pm - 8:00 pm
BOLIVIA		
La Paz	9.605	4:00 pm - 8:00 pm
La Paz	11.765	4:00 pm - 8:00 pm
BOTSWANA		
Francistown	5.965	4:00 pm - 5:00 pm
BRAZIL		
Rio de Janeiro	6.115	4:00 pm - 8:00 pm
Rio de Janeiro	9.720	4:00 pm - 8:00 pm
Rio de Janeiro	11.795	4:00 pm - 8:00 pm
Rio de Janeiro	15.295	4:00 pm - 8:00 pm
Rio de Janeiro	17.850	4:00 pm - 8:00 pm
BULGARIA		
Sofia	6.070	4:00 pm - 6:00 pm
Sofia	9.700	7:00 pm - 8:00 pm
Sofia	17.825	4:00 pm - 6:00 pm
BURMA		
Rangoon	7.120	7:00 pm - 8:00 pm

LOCATION	FREQ (MHz)	ACTUAL TIME
BURUNDI		
Bujumbura	6.140	4:00 pm - 5:00 pm
CAMBODIA		
Phnom-Penh	11.940	7:00 pm - 8:00 pm
CANADA		
Montreal	11.945	6:00 pm - 8:00 pm
Montreal	15.190	6:00 pm - 8:00 pm
Montreal	15.320	4:00 pm - 5:00 pm
Toronto	6.070	4:00 pm - 8:00 pm
CANARY ISLANDS		
Santa Cruz	11.800	4:00 pm - 8:00 pm
Santa Cruz	15.365	4:00 pm - 8:00 pm
CHILE		
Santiago	6.070	4:00 pm - 8:00 pm
Santiago	9.650	4:00 pm - 8:00 pm
Santiago	11.960	4:00 pm - 8:00 pm
CHINA (Taiwan)		
Minhsiung	7.150	7:00 pm - 8:00 pm
COLOMBIA		
Bogotá	5.960	4:00 pm - 8:00 pm
Bogotá	6.125	4:00 pm - 8:00 pm
CONGO, DEMOCRATIC REPUBLIC OF		
Kinshasa	7.185	4:00 pm - 8:00 pm
Kinshasa	15.245	4:00 pm - 8:00 pm
CONGO, PEOPLES REPUBLIC OF		
Brazzaville	6.115	4:00 pm - 6:00 pm
COOK ISLANDS		
Rarotonga	9.695	4:00 pm - 7:00 pm
Rarotonga	11.760	4:00 pm - 6:00 pm
COSTA RICA		
San José	6.007	6:00 pm - 8:00 pm
San José	9.645	4:00 pm - 8:00 pm
CUBA		
Havana	17.750	4:00 pm - 6:00 pm
DOMINICAN REPUBLIC		
Santo Domingo	6.090	4:00 pm - 8:00 pm
Santo Domingo	9.505	4:00 pm - 8:00 pm

LOCATION	FREQ (MHz)	ACTUAL TIME
ECUADOR		
Quito	9.745	4:00 pm - 8:00 pm
ENGLAND		
London	5.975	4:00 pm - 8:00 pm
London	6.110	5:00 pm - 8:00 pm
London	7.120	4:00 pm - 6:00 pm
London	9.580	4:00 pm - 8:00 pm
London	11.780	4:00 pm - 8:00 pm
FIJI ISLANDS		
Suva	5.955	4:00 pm - 5:00 pm
Suva	6.005	4:00 pm - 8:00 pm
FINLAND		
Helsinki	6.120	4:00 pm - 5:00 pm
Helsinki	15.185	6:00 pm - 7:00 pm
FRANCE		
Paris	6.175	4:00 pm - 5:00 pm
Paris	7.280	4:00 pm - 5:00 pm
Paris	15.120	4:00 pm - 7:00 pm
GERMAN DEMOCRATIC REPUBLIC		
Berlin	6.080	4:00 pm - 7:00 pm
Leipzig	9.730	4:00 pm - 7:00 pm
GERMANY, FEDERAL REPUBLIC OF		
Cologne	6.075	4:00 pm - 5:00 pm
Cologne	6.100	7:00 pm - 8:00 pm
Cologne	9.655	7:00 pm - 8:00 pm
Munich†	6.040	4:00 pm - 6:00 pm
Munich†	7.235	4:00 pm - 6:00 pm
Munich†	9.750	4:00 pm - 8:00 pm
Munich†	11.770	4:00 pm - 8:00 pm
Rohrdorf	7.265	4:00 pm - 7:00 pm
Stuttgart	6.030	4:00 pm - 7:00 pm
GHANA		
Tema	6.130	4:00 pm - 5:00 pm
Tema	9.545	4:00 pm - 6:00 pm
Tema	11.800	4:00 pm - 5:00 pm
GREECE		
Athens	9.710	4:00 pm - 5:00 pm
Athens	11.720	4:00 pm - 7:00 pm

†Radio Free Europe

LOCATION	FREQ (MHz)	ACTUAL TIME
GREENLAND		
Godthaab	5.960	4:00 pm - 8:00 pm
GRENADA		
St. George	11.970	6:00 pm - 8:00 pm
GUATEMALA		
Guatemala City	6.180	4:00 pm - 8:00 pm
GUINEA (Republic)		
Conakry	7.125	4:00 pm - 7:00 pm
Conakry	9.650	4:00 pm - 7:00 pm
GUYANA		
Georgetown	5.980	4:00 pm - 6:00 pm
HAITI		
Cap-Haitien	6.120	4:00 pm - 8:00 pm
Port-au-Prince	6.050	4:00 pm - 8:00 pm
HONDURAS		
Tegucigalpa	5.960	4:00 pm - 8:00 pm
Tegucigalpa	6.165	4:00 pm - 8:00 pm
HUNGARY		
Budapest	11.910	7:00 pm - 8:00 pm
Budapest	15.160	7:00 pm - 8:00 pm
INDIA		
Delhi	7.215	4:00 pm - 6:00 pm
INDONESIA		
Jakarta	6.045	6:00 pm - 8:00 pm
Jakarta	7.210	4:00 pm - 7:00 pm
IRAN		
Teheran	15.135	4:00 pm - 6:00 pm
IRAQ		
Baghdad	6.030	4:00 pm - 6:00 pm
Baghdad	7.180	4:00 pm - 6:00 pm
ISRAEL		
Jerusalem	7.190	4:00 pm - 5:00 pm
Jerusalem	9.625	4:00 pm - 5:00 pm
Jerusalem	9.725	4:00 pm - 5:00 pm
ITALY		
Rome	5.990	4:00 pm - 5:00 pm
Rome	6.010	5:30 pm - 7:00 pm
Rome	6.060	4:00 pm - 8:00 pm

LOCATION	FREQ (MHz)	ACTUAL TIME
ITALY (cont.)		
Rome	7.175	4:00 pm - 6:00 pm
Rome	9.515	4:00 pm - 8:00 pm
Rome	9.575	5:00 pm - 8:00 pm
Rome	9.710	5:30 pm - 7:00 pm
IVORY COAST		
Abidjan	7.210	4:00 pm - 7:00 pm
Abidjan	11.920	4:00 pm - 7:00 pm
JAPAN		
Tokyo	11.785	5:00 pm - 8:00 pm
Tokyo	15.445	5:00 pm - 6:00 pm
Tokyo	17.825	5:00 pm - 6:00 pm
JORDAN		
Amman	7.155	4:00 pm - 6:00 pm
Amman	11.810	4:00 pm - 6:00 pm
Amman	15.170	6:30 pm - 8:00 pm
KOREA		
Seoul	9.640	4:00 pm - 8:00 pm
LAOS		
Vientiane	6.130	4:00 pm - 8:00 pm
Vientiane	7.145	4:00 pm - 5:00 pm
		7:00 pm - 8:00 pm
LIBYA		
Tripoli	6.185	4:00 pm - 7:00 pm
Tripoli	7.165	4:00 pm - 8:00 pm
LUXEMBOURG		
Junglinster	6.090	4:00 pm - 8:00 pm
Junglinster	15.350	4:00 pm - 7:00 pm
MALAWI		
Zomba	5.995	4:00 pm - 5:00 pm
MALAYSIA		
Kuala Lumpur	9.725	5:00 pm - 8:00 pm
Kuala Lumpur	11.850	6:00 pm - 8:00 pm
MALI		
Bamako	9.745	4:00 pm - 6:00 pm
MARTINIQUE		
Fort-de-France	5.955	4:00 pm - 8:00 pm
MEXICO		
Leon	6.065	4:00 pm - 8:00 pm

LOCATION	FREQ (MHz)	ACTUAL TIME
MEXICO (cont.)		
Mexico City	6.055	7:00 pm - 8:00 pm
Mexico City	9.515	7:00 pm - 8:00 pm
Mexico City	9.530	7:00 pm - 8:00 pm
Mexico City	9.555	7:00 pm - 8:00 pm
Mexico City	11.718	7:00 pm - 8:00 pm
Mexico City	11.740	4:00 pm - 8:00 pm
Mexico City	11.820	4:00 pm - 8:00 pm
MONACO		
Monte Carlo	6.035	4:00 pm - 5:00 pm
Monte Carlo	7.135	4:00 pm - 5:00 pm
MOROCCO		
Tangier	6.170	4:00 pm - 8:00 pm
NETHERLANDS		
Hilversum	9.715	4:00 pm - 8:00 pm
Hilversum	11.730	5:00 pm - 8:00 pm
Hilversum	15.425	4:00 pm - 8:00 pm
NETHERLANDS ANTILLES		
Bonaire	9.590	7:00 pm - 8:00 pm
Bonaire	11.730	7:00 pm - 8:00 pm
NEW CALEDONIA		
Nouméa	7.170	4:00 pm - 8:00 pm
NEW HEBRIDES		
Vila	7.260	6:00 pm - 8:00 pm
NEW ZEALAND		
Wellington	15.110	4:00 pm - 7:00 pm
NICARAGUA		
Managua	5.935	7:00 pm - 8:00 pm
Managua	9.640	4:00 pm - 8:00 pm
Managua	9.710	4:00 pm - 8:00 pm
NIGERIA		
Enugu	9.595	4:00 pm - 6:00 pm
NORWAY		
Oslo	11.735	6:00 pm - 8:00 pm
Oslo	11.860	6:00 pm - 8:00 pm
PANAMA		
Panama City	9.685	4:00 pm - 8:00 pm
PAPUA		
Port Moresby	9.520	5:00 pm - 8:00 pm

LOCATION	FREQ (MHz)	ACTUAL TIME
PAPUA (cont.)		
Rabaul	5.985	6:00 pm - 8:00 pm
PARAGUAY		
Asunción	9.735	5:00 pm - 8:00 pm
Asunción	15.210	4:00 pm - 8:00 pm
PERU		
Lima	6.080	4:00 pm - 8:00 pm
Lima	9.560	4:00 pm - 8:00 pm
Lima	11.910	4:00 pm - 8:00 pm
Lima	15.150	4:00 pm - 8:00 pm
PHILIPPINES		
Manila	6.185	4:00 pm - 6:00 pm
Manila	9.715	5:00 pm - 7:00 pm
Manila	15.440	6:00 pm - 8:00 pm
Manila	17.810	5:00 pm - 7:00 pm
POLAND		
Warsaw	5.960	4:00 pm - 7:00 pm
Warsaw	5.970	4:00 pm - 8:00 pm
Warsaw	5.995	4:00 pm - 8:00 pm
Warsaw	6.035	4:00 pm - 8:00 pm
Warsaw	7.270	4:00 pm - 8:00 pm
Warsaw	9.525	4:00 pm - 7:00 pm
Warsaw	11.815	4:00 pm - 5:00 pm
PORTUGAL		
Lisbon	6.025	7:00 pm - 8:00 pm
Lisbon	9.565	4:00 pm - 6:00 pm
Lisbon	9.680	7:00 pm - 8:00 pm
Lisbon	11.935	7:00 pm - 8:00 pm
ROMANIA		
Bucharest	7.195	4:00 pm - 6:00 pm
Bucharest	9.510	4:00 pm - 8:00 pm
Bucharest	9.570	7:00 pm - 8:00 pm
RWANDA		
Kigali	15.410	6:00 pm - 8:00 pm
Kigali	15.435	4:00 pm - 5:00 pm
SAUDI ARABIA		
Mecca	6.000	4:00 pm - 6:00 pm
Mecca	9.670	4:00 pm - 6:00 pm
Mecca	15.150	4:00 pm - 5:00 pm

LOCATION	FREQ (MHz)	ACTUAL TIME
SENEGAL		
Dakar	11.895	4:00 pm - 7:00 pm
SINGAPORE		
Singapore	6.120	5:00 pm - 8:00 pm
Singapore	7.170	5:00 pm - 8:00 pm
Singapore	9.635	5:00 pm - 8:00 pm
Singapore	11.940	7:00 pm - 8:00 pm
SOUTH AFRICA		
Johannesburg	9.705	7:00 pm - 8:00 pm
Johannesburg	9.715	6:00 pm - 8:00 pm
Johannesburg	11.875	7:00 pm - 8:00 pm
Johannesburg	15.220	6:00 pm - 8:00 pm
SPAIN		
Madrid	7.105	4:00 pm - 5:00 pm
Madrid	9.570	4:00 pm - 5:00 pm
SUDAN		
Omdurman	7.200	4:00 pm - 5:00 pm
Omdurman	11.835	4:00 pm - 5:00 pm
SWITZERLAND		
Berne	6.055	4:00 pm - 6:00 pm
Berne	6.165	4:00 pm - 6:00 pm
SYRIA		
Damascus	9.660	4:00 pm - 5:00 pm
Damascus	11.860	6:00 pm - 8:00 pm
Damascus	15.290	4:00 pm - 6:00 pm
TOGO		
Lome	6.155	4:00 pm - 6:00 pm
Lome	7.265	4:00 pm - 6:00 pm
TUNISIA		
Tunis	6.195	4:00 pm - 7:00 pm
Tunis	11.970	4:00 pm - 7:00 pm
UGANDA		
Kampala	7.110	4:00 pm - 5:00 pm
UNITED ARAB REPUBLIC		
Cairo	7.265	4:00 pm - 8:00 pm
Cairo	9.550	4:00 pm - 8:00 pm
Cairo	9.740	4:00 pm - 7:00 pm
Cairo	11.890	4:00 pm - 7:00 pm

LOCATION	FREQ (MHz)	ACTUAL TIME
UNITED STATES OF AMERICA		
Delano*	17.765	4:00 pm - 8:00 pm
Greenville*	9.640	5:00 pm - 8:00 pm
Greenville*	11.740	4:00 pm - 5:00 pm
New York*	21.525	5:00 pm - 8:00 pm
URUGUAY		
Montevideo	6.125	4:00 pm - 8:00 pm
Montevideo	6.155	4:00 pm - 8:00 pm
Montevideo	9.595	6:00 pm - 8:00 pm
Montevideo	11.835	6:00 pm - 8:00 pm
U.S.S.R.		
Kursk	11.775	6:00 pm - 8:00 pm
Moscow	7.145	7:00 pm - 8:00 pm
Moscow	9.530	5:00 pm - 8:00 pm
Moscow	9.610	4:00 pm - 6:00 pm
Moscow	9.655	7:00 pm - 8:00 pm
Moscow	9.685	5:00 pm - 8:00 pm
Omsk	6.190	4:00 pm - 8:00 pm
Tallin	6.055	4:00 pm - 6:00 pm
Vladivostok	6.035	4:00 pm - 7:00 pm
U.S.S.R. (Ukranian)		
Ivanofrankovsk	9.665	5:00 pm - 8:00 pm
Ivanofrankovsk	9.760	5:00 pm - 8:00 pm
Simferopol	6.030	4:00 pm - 5:00 pm
VATICAN		
Vatican City	6.190	4:00 pm - 5:00 pm
Vatican City	9.615	7:00 pm - 8:00 pm
Vatican City	11.785	7:00 pm - 8:00 pm
Vatican City	15.285	7:00 pm - 8:00 pm
VENEZUELA		
Caracas	6.000	4:00 pm - 7:00 pm
Caracas	6.110	4:00 pm - 7:00 pm
Caracas	6.130	7:00 pm - 8:00 pm
Caracas	9.640	4:00 pm - 8:00 pm
Caracas	11.725	4:00 pm - 8:00 pm
Caracas	15.390	7:00 pm - 8:00 pm
VIETNAM		
Saigon	7.155	5:00 pm - 8:00 pm

*Voice of America

LOCATION	FREQ (MHz)	ACTUAL TIME
VIETNAM (cont.)		
Saigon	9.620	5:00 pm - 8:00 pm
Saigon	11.950	5:00 pm - 8:00 pm
YUGOSLAVIA		
Belgrade	6.100	4:00 pm - 8:00 pm
Belgrade	6.110	4:00 pm - 6:00 pm
Belgrade	6.150	4:00 pm - 7:00 pm
Belgrade	7.200	4:00 pm - 5:00 pm
Belgrade	7.240	4:00 pm - 8:00 pm
Belgrade	9.505	4:00 pm - 8:00 pm
Belgrade	9.620	4:00 pm - 7:00 pm
ZAMBIA		
Lusaka	6.165	4:00 pm - 5:00 pm

PART 6—8:00 pm–Midnight EST

LOCATION	FREQ (MHz)	ACTUAL TIME
AFGHANISTAN		
Kabul	6.000	9:00 pm - 11:00 pm
ALBANIA		
Tirana	6.200	8:00 pm - 11:00 pm
Tirana	7.300	8:00 pm - 11:00 pm
ANGOLA		
Luanda	7.265	8:00 pm - 9:00 pm
ARGENTINA		
Buenos Aires	6.060	8:00 pm - Midnight
Buenos Aires	9.690	8:00 pm - Midnight
ASCENSION		
Ascension	6.010	11:00 pm - Midnight
Ascension	9.510	8:00 pm - 11:00 pm
Ascension	11.820	8:00 pm - 11:00 pm
AUSTRALIA		
Darwin	7.190	8:00 pm - 9:00 pm
Melbourne	15.320	8:00 pm - Midnight
Melbourne	17.840	8:00 pm - 10:00 pm
Melbourne	21.740	8:00 pm - 10:00 pm

LOCATION	FREQ (MHz)	ACTUAL TIME
AUSTRIA		
Vienna	6.155	8:00 pm - Midnight
Vienna	9.770	8:00 pm - 11:00 pm
Vienna	17.715	11:00 pm - Midnight
BELGIUM		
Brussels	6.125	8:00 pm - 10:00 pm
Brussels	9.550	8:00 pm - 9:00 pm
BOLIVIA		
La Paz	9.605	8:00 pm - Midnight
La Paz	11.765	8:00 pm - 10:00 pm
BOTSWANA		
Francistown	5.965	11:00 pm - Midnight
BRAZIL		
Rio de Janeiro	6.115	8:00 pm - 10:00 pm
Rio de Janeiro	9.720	8:00 pm - 11:00 pm
Rio de Janeiro	11.795	8:00 pm - 11:00 pm
Rio de Janeiro	15.295	8:00 pm - 11:00 pm
Rio de Janeiro	17.850	8:00 pm - 11:00 pm
BULGARIA		
Sofia	9.700	8:00 pm - Midnight
BURMA		
Rangoon	9.685	11:00 pm - Midnight
BURUNDI		
Bujumbura	6.140	11:00 pm - Midnight
CAMBODIA		
Phnom-Penh	9.695	8:00 pm - 10:00 pm
Phnom-Penh	11.940	8:00 pm - 9:00 pm
Phnom-Penh	15.255	10:00 pm - 11:00 pm
CANADA		
Montreal	5.970	8:00 pm - Midnight
Montreal	9.625	9:00 pm - Midnight
Toronto	6.070	8:00 pm - Midnight
CANARY ISLANDS		
Santa Cruz	11.800	8:00 pm - 11:00 pm
Santa Cruz	15.365	8:00 pm - 11:00 pm
CEYLON		
Colombo	6.005	10:00 pm - Midnight
Colombo	9.670	8:00 pm - Midnight

LOCATION	FREQ (MHz)	ACTUAL TIME
NETHERLANDS		
Hilversum	9.545	10:00 pm - Midnight
Hilversum	11.730	8:00 pm - 9:00 pm
NETHERLANDS ANTILLES		
Bonaire	9.590	8:00 pm - Midnight
Bonaire	9.695	9:00 pm - 11:00 pm
Bonaire	11.730	8:00 pm - Midnight
Bonaire	15.345	9:00 pm - 11:00 pm
NEW CALEDONIA		
Nouméa	7.170	8:00 pm - 9:00 pm
NEW HEBRIDES		
Vila	7.260	8:00 pm - 10:00 pm
NICARAGUA		
Managua	5.935	8:00 pm - Midnight
Managua	9.640	8:00 pm - 10:00 pm
Managua	9.710	8:00 pm - 11:00 pm
NORWAY		
Oslo	9.550	8:00 pm - 10:00 pm
Oslo	9.610	8:00 pm - Midnight
Oslo	9.645	9:00 pm - 10:00 pm
PANAMA		
Panama City	9.685	8:00 pm - Midnight
PAPUA		
Port Moresby	9.520	8:00 pm - Midnight
Rabaul	5.985	8:00 pm - Midnight
PARAGUAY		
Asunción	9.735	8:00 pm - 10:00 pm
Asunción	15.210	8:00 pm - 10:00 pm
PERU		
Lima	6.080	8:00 pm - Midnight
Lima	9.560	8:00 pm - Midnight
Lima	11.910	8:00 pm - 11:00 pm
Lima	15.150	8:00 pm - 11:00 pm
PHILIPPINES		
Manila	15.440	8:00 pm - 9:00 pm
Manila	17.810	9:00 pm - Midnight
POLAND		
Warsaw	5.960	10:00 pm - Midnight

LOCATION	FREQ (MHz)	ACTUAL TIME
POLAND (cont.)		
Warsaw	5.970	8:00 pm - 10:00 pm
Warsaw	5.995	8:00 pm - 10:00 pm
Warsaw	6.035	8:00 pm - Midnight
Warsaw	7.270	8:00 pm - 11:00 pm
Warsaw	15.120	10:00 pm - Midnight
PORTUGAL		
Lisbon	6.025	8:00 pm - Midnight
Lisbon	7.215	11:00 pm - Midnight
Lisbon	9.680	8:00 pm - Midnight
Lisbon	11.935	8:00 pm - Midnight
RÉUNION		
Saint-Denis	7.245	11:00 pm - Midnight
ROMANIA		
Bucharest	9.510	8:00 pm - Midnight
Bucharest	9.570	8:00 pm - Midnight
Bucharest	11.940	9:00 pm - Midnight
RWANDA		
Kigali	15.410	8:00 pm - 9:00 pm
SAUDI ARABIA		
Mecca	6.000	10:00 pm - Midnight
Mecca	9.670	10:00 pm - Midnight
Mecca	11.855	10:30 pm - Midnight
Mecca	15.150	10:00 pm - Midnight
SINGAPORE		
Singapore	6.120	8:00 pm - Midnight
Singapore	7.170	8:00 pm - Midnight
Singapore	9.635	8:00 pm - Midnight
Singapore	11.940	8:00 pm - Midnight
SPAIN		
Madrid	6.140	8:00 pm - 11:00 pm
Madrid	9.760	8:00 pm - 11:00 pm
SOUTH AFRICA		
Johannesburg	9.705	8:00 pm - 11:00 pm
Johannesburg	9.715	8:00 pm - 11:00 pm
Johannesburg	11.875	8:00 pm - 11:00 pm
Johannesburg	15.220	8:00 pm - 11:00 pm
SUDAN		
Omdurman	7.200	10:00 pm - Midnight

LOCATION	FREQ (MHz)	ACTUAL TIME
SUDAN (cont.)		
Omdurman	11.835	10:00 pm - Midnight
SWITZERLAND		
Berne	6.120	9:00 pm - Midnight
SYRIA		
Damascus	11.860	8:00 pm - Midnight
Damascus	15.290	11:00 pm - Midnight
THAILAND		
Bangkok	7.135	10:00 pm - Midnight
Bangkok	11.910	11:00 pm - Midnight
TUNISIA		
Tunis	11.970	11:00 pm - Midnight
TURKEY		
Ankara	15.160	11:00 pm - Midnight
UGANDA		
Kampala	7.110	10:00 pm - Midnight
UNITED ARAB REPUBLIC		
Cairo	9.580	11:00 pm - Midnight
Cairo	9.625	8:00 pm - Midnight
UNITED STATES OF AMERICA		
Cincinnati*	11.810	8:00 pm - 11:00 pm
Delano*	17.765	8:00 pm - Midnight
Greenville*	11.845	10:00 pm - Midnight
URUGUAY		
Montevideo	6.125	8:00 pm - 11:00 pm
Montevideo	6.155	8:00 pm - 10:00 pm
Montevideo	9.595	8:00 pm - Midnight
Montevideo	11.835	8:00 pm - Midnight
Montevideo	15.274	8:00 pm - Midnight
U.S.S.R.		
Kursk	11.775	8:00 pm - Midnight
Moscow	7.145	8:00 pm - Midnight
Moscow	9.530	8:00 pm - Midnight
Moscow	9.610	11:00 pm - Midnight
Moscow	9.655	8:00 pm - Midnight
Moscow	9.685	8:00 pm - Midnight
Moscow	11.870	9:00 pm - Midnight
Moscow	17.880	11:00 pm - Midnight
Omsk	6.190	8:00 pm - 11:00 pm

*Voice of America

LOCATION	FREQ (MHz)	ACTUAL TIME
U.S.S.R. (cont.)		
Vladivostok	11.850	11:00 pm - Midnight
U.S.S.R. (Ukranian)		
Ivanofrankovsk	9.665	8:00 pm - Midnight
Ivanofrankovsk	9.760	8:00 pm - Midnight
Kiev	11.900	11:30 pm - Midnight
VATICAN		
Vatican City	9.615	8:00 pm - 9:00 pm
Vatican City	11.785	8:00 pm - 9:00 pm
Vatican City	15.285	8:00 pm - 9:00 pm
VENEZUELA		
Caracas	6.130	8:00 pm - 10:00 pm
Caracas	9.640	8:00 pm - 9:00 pm
Caracas	11.725	8:00 pm - 10:00 pm
Caracas	15.390	8:00 pm - Midnight
VIETNAM		
Saigon	7.155	8:00 pm - Midnight
Saigon	9.620	8:00 pm - Midnight
Saigon	11.950	8:00 pm - Midnight
YUGOSLAVIA		
Belgrade	6.100	8:00 pm - 9:00 pm
Belgrade	7.240	8:00 pm - 9:00 pm
Belgrade	9.505	8:00 pm - 9:00 pm
Belgrade	9.620	11:00 pm - Midnight
ZAMBIA		
Lusaka	6.165	11:00 pm - Midnight

SECTION 4

Clandestine Short-Wave Broadcasting Stations

LOCATION	IDENTIFICATION	FREQUENCY (MHz)
Cambodia	Voice of Khmer Freedom	4.910, 5.945, 6.067
Cyprus	Gazi Baf Radyosu	6.300
Greece	Radiofonikos Stathmos I Foni Tis Alithias	7.300, 7.335, 9.580 9.730, 9.775, 21.350
Iran	Peyk E. Iranian	6.025, 7.055, 9.560 11.410, 11.696
Iraq	Voice of IRAQI	6.037, 6.735, 6.915 7.027, 7.045, 7.195
Italy	Oggi in ITALIA	11.505
Korea (North)	Namjoson Haebang Pangsong	5.210
Laos	Withayu Kachai Siang Khana Pathet Lao	6.200, 6.230, 7.315 7.480, 8.600, 8.630
Latin America	Radio Libertad, La Voz Anti-communista de America	5.065, 6.240, 7.310 9.325, 15.050
Panama	Radio Rebelda Constitucion Alista	7.007
Portugal	Radio Portugal Livre	6.080, 8.332, 9.450 9.515, 11.510, 12.005 14.440, 15.485
Spain	Radio Espana Independiente	7.690, 8.333, 9.455
Thailand	Voice of the People of Thailand	6.035, 9.423
Turkey	Bizim Radyo	5.915, 9.500, 9.730
Vietnam	Dai Phat Thanh Giai Phong	5.200, 7.425, 10.225 10.260, 12.048

STATION LOG

LOCATION	FREQ.	TIME	REMARKS

STATION LOG

LOCATION	FREQ.	TIME	REMARKS

STATION LOG

LOCATION	FREQ.	TIME	REMARKS

STATION LOG

LOCATION	FREQ.	TIME	REMARKS

STATION LOG

LOCATION	FREQ.	TIME	REMARKS